5228 5.2

CANINE BEHAVIOR

CANINE BEHAVIOR

A History of Domestication; Behavioral Development and
Adult Behavior Patterns; Neurophysiology; Psychobiology;
Training, Inheritance, Early Experience and Psycho-Social
Relationships; Experimental Neuroses and Spontaneous
Behavioral Abnormalities; Congenital Anomalies and
Differential Diagnosis of Neurologic Disease

By

M. W. FOX, B. Vet. Med., M.R.C.V.S.

Medical Research Associate
Galesburg State Research Hospital
Galesburg, Illinois
Formerly, Postdoctoral Fellow
Jackson Laboratory
Bar Harbor, Maine

With a Foreword by

J. P. SCOTT

Senior Staff Scientist
Jackson Laboratory
Bar Harbor, Maine

CHARLES C THOMAS • PUBLISHER
Springfield • Illinois • U.S.A.

Published and Distributed Throughout the World by

CHARLES C THOMAS • PUBLISHER

Bannerstone House

301-327 East Lawrence Avenue, Springfield, Illinois, U.S.A.

Natchez Plantation House

735 North Atlantic Boulevard, Fort Lauderdale, Florida, U.S.A.

With THOMAS BOOKS careful attention is given to all details of manufacturing and design. It is the Publisher's desire to present books that are satisfactory as to their physical qualities and artistic possibilities and appropriate for their particular use. THOMAS BOOKS will be true to those laws of quality that assure a good name and good will.

DEDICATION
To my parents

FOREWORD

T HE DOG is probably the oldest domestic animal, having associated with man for 8,000 to 10,000 years. Despite this close relationship, and almost universal distribution throughout the world, the dog is still in many ways scientifically unknown. It is only within recent years that we have begun to accumulate accurate knowledge regarding its behavior and development. In this book Dr. Fox has made an extensive survey of available literature relating to the neurological basis of behavioral development and has presented it in a form which should be highly useful for both the veterinary practitioner and practical breeder. Of particular interest is Dr. Fox's own study of the development of reflexes and the clinical application of this information.

Small animal practice is rapidly becoming a major proportion of veterinary work, and the practitioner is often called upon to deal with problems which have psychological as well as biological causes. There is room for a specialty in veterinary medicine dealing with abnormal behavior in animals and corresponding somewhat to the practice of psychiatry in the human field. I hope that Dr. Fox's volume will be a real aid to progress in this direction.

The careful reader will note that some of the results and opinions expressed by scientists are contradictory, and that not all of these contradictions have been resolved. This reflects the fact that there is still an immense amount of unexplored scientific territory connected with dog behavior and calls attention to the need for additional research.

J. P. SCOTT
Senior Staff Scientist
Jackson Laboratory

PREFACE

THE MOST significant findings in behavioral development, neurophysiology, and psychobiology of the dog have been brought together in this book to serve as a reference source for the comparative psychologist, neurophysiologist and veterinary clinician. Normal behavioral development of the dog, as studied psychologically and neurologically, is reviewed, and particular regard is given to the events that lead to the onset of the critical period of socialization. Normal behavior patterns of the adult dog will be described in detail, and behavioral abnormalities due to inherited or acquired factors will be discussed. Again particular emphasis will be made on the behavioral abnormalities that may arise as a result of psychological trauma during the period when primary social relationships are made in the domestic environment. Also experimentally induced abnormalities will be briefly included. The understanding of social behavior in animals may contribute to the understanding of human behavior and experiments will be described in which dogs have been used in psychobiological research to throw light on mental health problems in man. Special attention will be focused on the normal rearing and training of the dog and the diagnosis, treatment, or prophylaxis of spontaneous (clinical and not experimentally induced) behavioral abnormalities discussed in detail.

Present knowledge in the field of psychobiology of the dog will be reviewed to meet the needs of the veterinarian in a changing world of medicine, where psychiatric and psychosomatic disease problems are challenging the clinician in human medicine. Animals are useful tools for experimentation to investigate these problems in man and are being used with increasing intensity in many research programs such as neurophysiology, behavioral development and psychobiology. From such experiments useful data have been collected, and in many instances these results have direct applications to problems in veterinary medicine. Normal adult behavior patterns and symptoms associated with experimentally induced behavior disorders are described, and in relation to these norms the etiology of spontaneous behavior disorders are discussed. This should interest the veterinarian, for much time is given to the differential diagnosis of organic disease from behavioral disorder.

Chapters dealing with the history of domestication, training, inheritance, and the selection of breed type to perform particular tasks are incorporated to illustrate the several relationships between man and dog at the psychosocial level and should interest a wide range of readers, from the dog trainer to the sociologist. Changes in society and way of life cause alterations in these relationships and in the selection of breed type, so that the individual reflects much of his psychosocial background in the type of dog kept.

Studies of canine-human relationships such as "child substitution" and overdependency will be discussed at the sociological level.

It is hoped that this book will establish a scientific background for the interpretation of canine behavior by professional people concerned with dog training and treatment of behavioral abnormalities. There has been much concern recently at the increase in the number of people claiming to be "canine psychiatrists" and practicing "psychiatry" on canine patients. Although it is of concern where these people received their formal training, more important is the fact that canine patients do develop behavioral abnormalities, and properly qualified individuals in the veterinary field should be able to give advice on these cases. He may not wish to undertake corrective training (a better term than psychotherapy!), and, indeed, there are many specialized dog trainers (not psychiatrists) who are competent to do this. Cases of abnormal behavior in the canine species are frequently reported and there is a growing need for some understanding of the etiology and treatment of these conditions.

Development of behavior and the nervous system is described in detail, and these indices of normality could be applied to future research on the effects of early experience (e.g., radiation of the pregnant dam) on later behavior. The psychobiologist will find useful references on normality in this context. Russian work on the different types of nervous system (varying degrees of strength and excitability) and modern Pavlovian concepts are presented in this book and compared to similar experiments by researchers in the West, who approach their problems by different concepts and methods, but frequently obtain significantly comparable results. Abnormalities in behavior, experimentally induced by such means as radiation or emotional stress during critical periods of development in utero must be investigated for the future well being of mankind, who is exposed to an everchanging physical and social environment. Any correlates of behavioral development that can be found in many species of animals may be extrapolated and interpolated to clarify theoretical impressions and support established concepts of child development.

The animal correlate of the human norm may then be manipulated experimentally and these results would formulate a scientific approach to therapy. Indices of normality may therefore be used as criteria for interpreting behavioral abnormality.

CONTENTS

CANINE BEHAVIOR

Chapter 1

THE HISTORY OF DOMESTICATION

Origin

THE ORIGIN of the domestic dog is obscure. All dogs belong to a single genus, *Canis*. The wolf (*Canis lupus*) is thought to be the most likely ancestor of the dog. (Matthew 1930; Colbert 1939) This species was distributed widely throughout Europe, Asia and North America in earlier times. Present day wild packs differ from locality to locality in both coat color and body size. The jackal was once thought to be a possible ancestor of some types of domesticated dog, but on morphological grounds (notably similar skull features) it is thought that the dog probably originated from the wolf. More distant relatives of the domesticated dog are the foxes (vulpes) and wild dogs such as the dhole of India, the South American bush dog and the African hunting dog.

An excellent study of the wolf in its natural environment (Scott 1950) revealed that several aspects of wolf behavior may still be found in the domestic dog. The wolf patterns of behavior in all domestic dogs have been accentuated or reduced in different breeds (Scott 1954), for selection has taken place to evolve breeds to perform specialized activities such as hunting, guarding, herding, guide dogs for the blind, and as pets for human companionship (see Chapter 4).

Historic Evidence

Some early signs of domestication were found in Denmark (Degerbol 1927). Skeletal remains were excavated from a Middle Stone Age settlement, and these remains resemble in several

aspects, the skeleton of the modern *Canis familiaris*. These bones
are thought to date back to probably 7,000 B.C. Dog remains have
been found in Egyptian tombs dating back to 6,000 B.C. (Haag
1948) and from 6,500-8,500 B.C. (Reed 1959). In Australia the
dingo is thought to have originated many thousands of years ago
and was probably brought into the continent as a domesticated
animal of some nomadic tribes. Since then it has gone wild, but
some dingos are found semi-domesticated in aborigine camps, or
crossbred with local modern-day dogs.

In Africa, the Basenji was a hunting dog of pygmy tribes,
and is still used by these people. Possibly this dog was taken to
Egypt, for related species are found there today. The Egyptians
are noted in history for their reverence for the cat, and the dog,
and these animals have been included in several of their religious
art works (see Figure 3). A dog-headed god was part of their
religious culture.

In the sixteenth century Caius in England wrote a descrip-
tion of English dogs which included the greyhound, which originated from Mesopotamia, hounds, sporting dogs, terriers, mastiffs
and shepherd dogs, and small household pet dogs.

Many ancient breeds have disappeared, but in Iraq the
Saluki and Kurdish herding dog are still found. The Kurdish
resembles the large mastiff-like hunting and war dogs depicted
in Babylonian art over 2,000 B.C. (see Figures 1 and 2).

When early settlers came to America, several breeds already
kept by the North American Indians, Eskimos and Mexicans
were found (Allen 1920). The Eskimo sled dog and the Mexican
hairless dogs are the only two remaining breeds, the former
probably being a cross between wolf and spitz type of dog.

Domestication and Selection

How did the relationship between man and dog first come
about? This we will never know, but one may speculate that
primitive man realized the hunting potentials of the dog and
reared puppies which were socialized and were later trained to
perform tasks such as hunting, tracking and pursuing quarry,
defending the settlement and domesticated farm stock from
marauding wolves and other predators. Also the dog was used as

Figure 1. Hunting scene from Nineveh, 668-626 B.C. (Courtesy the British Museum.)

food and was regarded as a delicacy by American Indians; the chow-chow is still eaten in China.

As the settlements enlarged and civilizations and cultures grew, two important things took place. Firstly, exploration of

Figure 2. Mastiff of Babylon (2nd millennium). (Courtesy the British Museum.)

Figure 3. Egyptian dogs from Rizeikat (2280-2240 B.C.). (Courtesy the trustees, Boston Museum of Fine Arts.)

distant countries, trading and invasions occurred, and with man went his dog, resulting in the dissemination of indigenous breeds of dogs to other areas. Secondly, social factors caused selection of breeds for different tasks; hunting, guard, and war dogs were bred, and also pet dogs for companionship. Four thousand years ago the Egyptians and Babylonians had greyhound-like hunting dogs, and mastiffs for hunting larger game and for war. The Jews had two breeds which they were forbidden by law to crossbreed. One was a small house dog and another was a guard or hunting dog. In Greece, records of different types of dog dating back to 400 B.C. have been found. Heavy greyhounds for hunting and small whippet and spitz-type Pomeranians for household pets were kept.

In Europe there are few historical remains that give much evidence of the types of domestic dogs that were bred. Cave paintings in Brittany depict some dogs perhaps participating with man in hunting, but, other than this, the earliest evidence is of a Great dane-like dog on the Crinobeline coin from England, dated approximately 43 A.D. During the Roman invasion of Britain, the light greyhound-type Roman dog was bred with the heavier indigenous hunting dog which was used to hunt boar and other large game. These powerful British dogs were used for bull baiting in Roman arenas, according to Claudian the historian.

In Cromwell's time, bull fighting and bear baiting were popular sport in Britain. The bulldog, bull mastiff and bull terrier are present day breeds that were once used in these sports. Undoubtedly Great Britain is, historically, the most prolific country for the selective breeding of a great variety of dogs. By the nineteenth century a full complement of breeds was to be found (Hodgman 1963) fitting a variety of tasks including sporting (setters, pointers and spaniels), small sporting (bull terrier and fox terrier), shepherding (old English and Scottish collie), coursing (greyhounds), hounds for sight and smell hunting (greyhounds, wolf, fox and other hounds and beagles) and guard dogs (mastiff) and pets (King Charles spaniel, pug and pomeranian). The sporting breeds originally came from a medieval spaniel type. The large griffon was developed in the Netherlands and the weimaraner in Germany. The hounds that hunted by sight were bred from a near-east greyhound type crossed with a larger indigenous mastiff. The borzoi, Irish wolfhound and Scottish deerhound are related animals of this type. The scent hounds came from a Harrier type, from which we have the beagle, fox hound, bloodhound and otterhound. The dachshund was developed in Germany as a hound-terrier to hunt badgers. The standard poodle was developed from a spaniel type gun dog. The Norwegian elkhound is a different type of hound, originating from a spitz type.

The working dogs, used for shepherding, guarding and light draft work are more variable, depending on their country of origin. The collie, shetland sheepdog and Welsh corgi are used in England, the German shepherd in Germany. Guard dogs are also of miscellaneous origin, such as a Newfoundland, great dane, Pyrenees, St. Bernard and doberman pinscher. The samoyed, Siberian husky and Alaskan malemute are sled dogs from various arctic regions.

The terrier is a notable English type of dog used for hunting vermin and as a small watch dog for the household. Over twenty different breeds are recognized.

The toy breeds are of variable origin and include the pekingese of China, Chihuahua of Mexico, Italian greyhound, and smaller version of larger breeds such as the minature poodle, sheltie, the pug (which came to Holland from China), miniature spaniels, e.g., King Charles; miniature terriers, e.g., toy Manchester terrier; and miniature spitz types, e.g., papillion. Three skull types are present in this group, namely the mesocephalic (normal), dolichocephalic (long faced) and mutant brachycephalic (short faced). These morphological differences in relation to selective breeding and undesirable characteristics of the breed will be discussed in Chapter 4.

More recent breeds have arisen, such as the Boston terrier, bluetick and redbone coonhounds, and the Australian kelpie, which are local dogs. As the needs of a particular variety for working or for "miniaturization" into toy-pet dogs continues, we may see further changes and the introduction of newly and officially recongized breeds.

Zeuner (1963) has given an extensive review of the archaeological evidence for domestication of the dog in his classical book on the history of domesticated animals. He refers to the earliest signs of domestication in some remains dated by radiocarbon evidence at 8,000 B.C. He is of the opinion that hunting and scavenging activities established a social bond or commensal relationship between primitive dog and man. The earliest known dog remains are similar to the dingo and Zeuner suggests the following evolutionary tree, although he is careful to point out that evidence is by no means conclusive and that the domesticated dog most probably sprang from one of the geographical races of the wolf.

(Slightly modified, from Zeuner, 1963.)

Zeuner advances an important effect of domestication and selection which he calls neoteny, or the persistence of juvenile characteristics. These immature features (e.g., small head and body size, reduced canines and drooping ears) were selected and are prominent characteristics of the pet breeds like the pomeranian originating from Canis familiaris palustris. Such anatomical immaturity is seen in several present day breeds which also show varying degrees of behavioral neoteny. Selective breeding has produced these strains for owners who wish to indulge their pets which are maintained as dependent care-seeking perpetual "juveniles". (see Chapter 8).

Dechambre, (1949), has explored a similar theory that race formation in the dog and pig has been facilitated by the phenomenon of "fetalization." Selection for more docile or "un-wild" characteristics through generations of breeding has given us a wide variety of domestic strains that differ from their wild ancestors, for they lack the greater physical development of the wild species. Immaturity or arrested development, both behaviorally (e.g., weak pack behavior) and anatomically (e.g., reduced canine teeth) in the dog, has occurred as a result of domestication and selection for these charactertistics. Hematologic studies of blood groups of different breeds show that over a wide variety of breed types, differing greatly in physical characteristics, variations in blood groups are few; only five different blood groups (isoantibodies) are recognized in the dog. Cohen and Fuller (1958) have studied the inheritance of blood groups in the dog and find that the different types are inherited by a simple Mendelian mechanism.

Also the facility with which mating between the domestic dog and wolves and wild canidae occurs may indicate again a common ancestry (Dice, 1942; Iljin, 1941). Behavorial differences are not so great as to cause incompatibility between these species, and similarity of reproductive mechanisms allows fertile matings to take place (see Chapter 4).

References

Allen, G. M.: Dogs of American Aborigines. *Bull. Mus. Comp. Zool.* Harvard *63*:431-517, 1920.

Cohen, C. & Fuller, J. L.: The inheritance of blood types in the dog. *J. Hered., 44*:225-228, 1953.

Colbert, E. H.: Origin of the dog. *Natural History, 43*:90-101, 1939.

Dechambre, E.: La theorie de foetalization et la formation des races de chiens et de porc. *Mammalia, 13*:129-137, 1949.

Degerbol, M.: Uber prähistorische dänische Hunde. *Vidensk. Meddel. Dansk Naturhist. For. Kobenhavn, 84*:17-72, 1927.

Dice, L. R.: A family of dog-coyote hybrids. *J. Mammal. 23*:186-192, 1942.

Haag, W. G.: An osteometric analysis of some aboriginal dogs. *Univ. Kentucky Rep. Anthrop., 7*:107-264, 1948.

Hodgman, D. A.: Short history of dogs from 3000 B.C. to A.D. 1962. Animal Health, 1. 2. 49-56, 1963.

Iljin, N. A.: Wolf-dog genetics. *J. Genetics, 42*:359-414, 1941.

Matthew, W. D.: The phylogeny of dogs. *J. Mammal., 11*:117-138, 1930.

Reed, C. A.: Animal domestication in the Prehistoric near east. Science, 130. 1629-1639, 1959.

Scott, J. P.: The social behavior of dogs and wolves: an illustration of sociobiological systems. *Ann. New York Acad. Sc., 51*:1009-1021, 1950.

Scott, J. P.: The effects of selection and domestication upon behavior of the dog. *J. Nat Cancer Inst., 15*:3:739-758, 1954.

Zeuner, F. E.: *The History of Domesticated Animals.* England, Hutchins, 1963.

Chapter 2

DEVELOPMENT OF BEHAVIOR AND NEURO-ONTOGENY OF THE DOG

THE STUDY OF behavioral development in the newly born organism has several important applications. One may learn how an animal, after birth, adapts to its environment both physiologically and psychologically, and, by comparing criteria of established indices of normal development, we may understand the mechanisms involved in the genesis of abnormal behavior. "Psychological trauma" during a critical period may affect later behavior, and the dog serves as an excellent research animal for this purpose. Homeostasis is well developed in precocious neonates like the ruminants, and correlated with these almost adult-like physiological mechanisms, allowing greater environmental independence, such animals are behaviorally more advanced, and immediately after birth establish psycho-social relationships with their own species. As sensory and motor abilities are well developed, imprinting and the following response are established soon after birth (Hess 1958). In contrast, the carnivora are nonprecocious and at birth have poorly developed homeostatic mechanisms, and sensory and motor abilities are minimal, so that psycho-social relationships do not develop until much later in the postnatal period of development.

In newly hatched goslings, a following response to any moving object (man, or the parent goose) occurs, and goslings will follow the first moving object they see after hatching. As sensory and motor abilities are well developed, especially visual and locomotor, psycho-social relationships are immediately established after hatching. This is termed imprinting, and occurs at a certain

time, after which no following response or imprinting occurs
(Collias, 1952; Lorenz, 1935). In other birds hatched within the
nest (altricial or immature when hatched), similar imprinting
occurs as primary social relationships are established with its own
species, although no following response is present. This sensitive
time is a critical period for the development of primary socialization, and is common to all precocious animals. At a later age,
subsequent following of other animals is prevented by the development of a fear response (to moving objects).

A short period in early development therefore exists, during
which time primary social relationships may be made, dependent
upon the degree of sensory and motor maturation characteristic
of the species concerned. As these mechanisms are well developed
at birth in precocious animals, primary socialization occurs earlier
than in non-precocious animals, which require a longer period of
nursing and are environmentally less independent. The newborn
dog is in this latter group, and at birth, behavior is adapted to
maintain maximal contact with the mother by a spectrum of
reflexes and innate behavioral mechanisms (Fox, 1963a) which
we shall later discuss in detail.

Behavioral development and primary socialization (the time
during which the first psycho-social relationships are established)
in an animal such as the dog is well supported by similar studies
in other species, where certain periods during development are
critical to the formation of social relationships. This is the critical period hypothesis, and the neurologic and behavioral development leading up to the onset of this period will now be described.

Critical Periods of Development

The periods of behavioral development in the dog have been
described by Scott (1958; 1962). These periods are characterized
by behavior patterns which are limited by the degree of sensory
and motor development (see Figure 1). Changes in behavior
point to some developmental change in sensory-motor ability and
the onset of a new critical period. These periods have been di-
vided into Neontal (birth-13 days); Transitional (13-19 days);
and Socialization (19 days-12 weeks) periods of development,
determined by behavioral observations only. There is considerable

Table of Critical Periods of Development in the Dog

Period		Dura-tion (days)	Behavior	CNS	Reflexes
N E O N A T A L	I	0-14	Neonatal nutrition.	Motor cortex most developed part of cortex. Dry matter of brain 10%. Slow growth of cerebral hemispheres.	Change from fetal to neonatal responses. Flexion—Extension of hind limbs. Magnus reflex. Rooting reflex. Cross Extensior reflex. Reflex urination.
T R A N S I T I O N A L	II	14-21	Unstable conditioning. Eyes open (vision poor). No startle reflex to sound. Transition to motor sensory and psychological capacities of adult.	Rapid differentiation of specific cortical areas and rapid increase in growth. Dry matter 12%. EEG no differentiation between sleep and waking (no alpha rhythm).	Neonatal reflexes. Slight variability due to central inhibition and fear responses.
S O C I A L I Z A T I O N	III	21-70	Stable conditioning. Startle reflex to sound. Positive audio-visual orientation reflex and visual cliff response. Formation of primary social relationships (notices observer, play and fear responses, etc.)	Alpha rhythm in EEG appears. Growth of cortex continues rapidly up to 42 days then more gradually. Dry matter 20% at 56 days. Adult EEG at 49-56 days.	No reflex urination and rooting reflex weakens. Magnus and crossed extensor reflexes disappear and adult reflexes remain and fore and hind limb supporting reactions become stronger.
J U V E N I L E	IV	70-onwards	Weaning. Maturation of locomotor abilities and equilibratory responses. Growth and development of motor skills.	Final maturation of CNS.	Adult reflexes and responses.

Figure 1. Table of critical periods of development.

overlap between the termination of one phase and the onset of a new phase of behavior. The critical period of socialization commences at approximately three weeks of age, reaching a peak between five and seven weeks. Sensory and motor changes at this time include the development of visual and auditory abilities and adult patterns of locomotion, clearly distinguishable from the more primitive activities of the neonate. With such increased abilities the animal becomes more independent and is able to explore its environment and so establish primary social relationships and form positive or negative emotional responses.

Correlations have been made between a spectrum of reflexes (Thomas, 1940; James, 1952; Fox, 1963 a & 1964e) and physiologic and anatomic development of the brain (Fox, 1963d) and spinal cord to determine how well temporal changes in these correlates compared with the overt behavioral development as described by Scott.

Developmental changes in the categories of reflexes will be described in relation to periods of neural development, which will be found to correlate well with the behavioral periods of development.

Development of Reflexes and Behavior

Period 1 (0-5 Days)

Sensory Motor Responses. The crossed extensor (pinching one hind leg causes flexion while the opposite leg extends) and Magnus reflexes (twisting the head to one side causes extension of the limbs on the side toward which the head is turned while the opposite limbs are flexed) can be elicited immediately after birth and throughout this period. The rooting reflex and negative geotactic (see Figs. 2 and 3) responses are easier to demonstrate as locomotor ability improves up to four days of age. Muscle tone is determined by manipulation of the limbs and observing the posture assumed by the limbs and spinal column. At birth, muscle tone is flaccid but as independent respiration is established, muscle tone increases rapidly, with dominance of the flexor muscles over the extensors. Consequently, reflex extension of the limbs during stimulation of the crossed extensor and Magnus reflexes is reduced while flexion of the opposite limbs is increased. Hyperkinesias (random motor movements or twitches) are seen affecting the body and face during this period.

Fore limb contactual placing reactions are first seen as weak and variable responses between two and three days onwards.

The palpebral blink response to a light touch on the eyelids is present, but the latency of response is much greater than in the adult, a slow palpebral contraction occurring some time after the tactile stimulus.

Head turning is slow when testing the auriculonasocephalic reflex. (Tickling one side of the face causes head turning toward

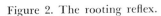
Figure 2. The rooting reflex.

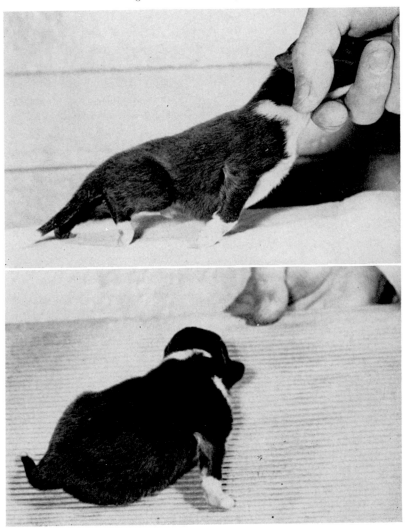
Figure 3. Negative geotaxic response.

the side stimulated, i.e., a positive thigmotaxic response). Towards the end of this period these reflexes are easier to evoke and
the responses are stronger. Constant stimulation of the head, elicit-
ing the rooting reflex, results in forward progression, and a newborn pup may cover a distance of over fifty yards without showing signs of fatigue.

At birth, the nociceptive (pain) withdrawal response to
pinching a hind foot is slow and sustained; squirming, side to side
flexion of the trunk, and prolonged distress vocalization are
characteristic of the newborn dog. Reflex urination is easily
elicited by stroking the external genitalia; stimulation of respiration (increased rate and depth of ventilation) is also seen when
these areas are stimulated during this period. Reflex defacation
can be similarly evoked.

Organs of Special Sense (Visual and Auditory Responses).
No sensory responses of the audiovisual system can be elicited
until two to four days of age when the palpebral blink response
to light (photomotor reflex) is first seen as a slow and easily
fatigued response with a long latency.

Period II (5-18 Days)

Sensory Motor Reflexes. The crossed extensor reflex can no
longer be elicited at eighteen days of age. The Magnus reflex ceases
to affect the fore limbs after fourteen days, but still affects the hind
limbs at eighteen days. Further changes in muscle tone occur at
the onset of this period. Extensor dominance causing hind limb
extension and opisthotonus (extension of the spine) persists until
eighteen days of age (see Fig. 4).

Gross hyperextension of the hind limbs with extreme hyper-
tonia, opisthotonus and pointing of the hind feet is commonly
seen and is considered a normal variable at this age during the
period of extensor dominance.

Fore limb supporting reactions are first seen between six and
ten days and hind limb supporting between eleven and fifteen
days as weak and variable responses, just after the emergence of
hind limb placing reactions at eight days. Hyperkinesias were
restricted mainly to the head during this time.

Few changes occur in the superficial reflexes during this
second period.

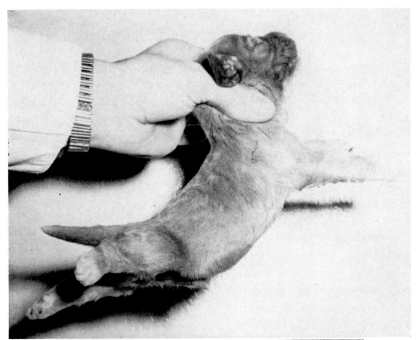

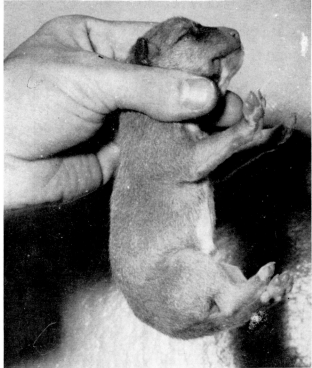

Figure 4. Changes in muscle tone with age. Upper figure: Extensor phase (5-18 days). Lower figure: Flexor phase (0-5 days).

Reflex stimulation of respiration is no longer seen when the anogenital regions are stimulated.

Head turning and orientation towards the side stimulated is rapid, and during elicitation of the labial reflex the finger may be seized and sucked.

The rooting reflex is weaker and more variable at about fourteen days of age onwards; this is associated with opening of the eyes and development of the ability to walk backwards. Strong responses are obtained if the animal is made fearful of the situation, e.g., by pinching the tail.

This avoidance behavior is first seen during this period; nociceptive withdrawal responses after stimulating a hind foot causes less lateral flexion and vocalization is less protracted. The animal attempts to escape from the situation.

Sense Organs. Although the eyes begin to open between ten and sixteen days the blink response is not adult-like until eighteen days of age. Weak auditory startle responses are seen at eighteen days when the neonate is asleep, but are variable and absent when the animal is awake or feeding.

Period III (18-28 Days)

Sensory Motor Reflexes. The Magnus reflex ceases to affect the hind limbs by twenty-one days. Extensor muscle dominance in the hind limbs rapidly weakens from eighteen days onward, giving rise to normal distribution of muscle tone between the flexor and extensor muscles. As reciprocal muscle tone becomes more evenly distributed, motor strength increases equally after the onset of normotonia.

Maintenance of posture (equilibration) when subjected to see-saw tilting is initially poor and the blindfold animal cannot maintain an upright posture when tilted anteroposteriorly (occipitofrontal) until between twenty-five and twenty-eight days of age. The ability to remain upright when subjected to lateral (bitemporal) tilting is poorly developed throughout this period.

When held upside down and dropped (blindfolded) the righting response in space as determined by the animal's ability to land on all fours is seen as a weak and variable response at this time.

Facial hyperkinesias disappear completely by four weeks of age.

These reflexes are difficult to elicit at this time. The labial sucking reflex disappears by twenty-one days but in some undernourished pups it persists until five to six weeks of age, as does the auriculonasocephalic and rooting reflexes which normally disappear after three weeks of age.

Reflex urination after stimulating the external genitalia becomes weak and variable at three weeks and disappears by four weeks.

Avoidance behavior is marked when the pain withdrawal reflex is stimulated.

Sense Organs. This period is marked by the emergence of positive orientation responses to visual and auditory stimuli which are strong at twenty-five days of age and adult-like thereafter.

Period IV (28 Days Onwards)

Sensory Motor Reflexes. A transition from variable locomotor responses to adult-like postural and equilibratory abilities now occurs. Not until five to six weeks of age is it possible for the animal to maintain an upright posture when subjected to bitemporal tilting. The righting response becomes more efficient and these adult locomotor abilities improve during this final period of motor development. Similarly the hopping reaction improves and all earlier motor responses are more rapidly elicited.

This period is characterized by the complete disappearance of primitive superficial reflexes which are an integral part of neonatal behavior. The sucking, rooting, and auriculonasocephalic reflexes are no longer demonstrable. Each response is adult-like in character where localization of response and variability due to emotional reactions occur concurrently.

Sense Organs. Positive visual cliff reactions are first seen reliably at twenty-eight days of age (see Fig. 5) ; visual and auditory recognition of littermates and observer occurs in association with the emergence of approach and avoidance behavior.

Briefly, some reflexes are initially strong and stereotyped, but as higher nervous centers develop they become more variable, due in part to central inhibition and to emotional reactions arising from the experimental situation. By four weeks of age these reflexes either disappear as behavior changes, or become stable and

Figure 5. The visual cliff apparatus, for depth discrimination studies.

assume the characteristics of the adult animal.

To summarize these results the main reflex changes were recorded during the following periods.

Period I (0-5 days).

    Disappearance of flexor dominance and respiratory skin stimulation.

Period II (5-18 days).

    5-13 days—appearance of adult postural reflexes.

    15-18 days—disappearance of crossed extensor and Magnus reflexes.

Period III (18-28 days).

    Disappearance of rooting and reflex urination.

    Appearance of adult sensory (startle, visual cliff) reactions and motor activities.

By comparing these neurologic periods with the behavioral periods of development (see Fig. 6) we see that changes from one neurologic period to another precede the observed behavorial changes, and we may surmise that development of the nervous system occurs prior to the emergence of a new behavior pattern.

The elicitation of some of these reflexes may be used clinically to assess the extent of a neurologic defect or arrested development of the higher nervous system (Fox, 1963 b & c). In the developing animal, several primitive reflexes may persist in severe

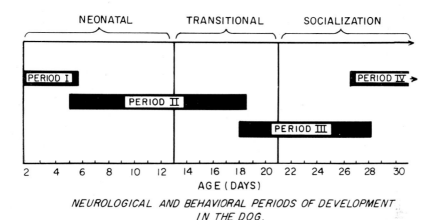

NEUROLOGICAL AND BEHAVIORAL PERIODS OF DEVELOPMENT IN THE DOG.

Figure 6. Comparison of neurologic and behavioral periods of development.

hydrocephaly for example, as higher nervous processes do not develop. Similarly, in the adult, an extensive lesion (neoplastic or traumatic) may damage the fore-brain and cause the sudden appearance of primitive reflexes as the damping or inhibitory effect of the higher nervous control is destroyed either partially or completely.

Remarkably similar is the neurologic development of the human infant, where primitive foetal posture, crossed extensor and Magnus reflexes are found in the neonate, and later disappear as the nervous system develops (Gessel, 1945; Thomas et al., 1961). Similar phenomena of flexor and extensor muscle dominance have also been described (Ingram, 1959). Comparable neurologic periods of development may also be evident in other mammals, but as yet these have not been studied in detail except in the mouse, where three neurologic periods of development have been found to correlate with similar behavioral periods (Kobayashi et al., 1963; Williams and Scott, 1953).

The Growing Brain

Histologic studies of the nervous system of the dog have given some interesting evidence of the sequential changes occurring during postnatal development. Examination of the spinal cord using Nissl stains to show up the neurons and luxol blue stain to pick up myelin sheaths on the nerve tracts reveal that at birth and until three weeks of age the neurons contain little Nissl substance (in other words, they are still immature) and myelinization of the ventral motor horn tracts is minimal. At four weeks of age the features of the spinal cord almost resemble the adult animal and by five weeks there is maximal concentration of myelin and the neurons are morphologically indistinguishable from the adult animal (Fox. 1964f). Myelin is associated with the speed of conduction of nerve impulses, and it is not until four weeks of age that adult-like responses are seen in the reflexes and locomotor patterns of the hind limbs. Increasing concentrations of myelin probably indicate an increasing approach to adult functional capacity (Langworthy, 1933). Myelin is also almost completely absent in the brains of newborn puppies except in those portions connected with certain cranial nerves, namely the trigeminal facial and non-acoustic portion of the auditory nerve (Harman, 1963). One may conclude that the development of myelin corresponds to the observed behavioral function in the newborn, since these nerves are concerned with feeding, head orientation (rooting and thigmotaxis), and geotactic and righting responses respectively.

Gross examination of the cerebral cortex at different ages has given further correlates which suggest rapid postnatal development of the brain during the first four weeks of life, after which development is more gradual, reaching apparent maturity at six to seven weeks (Fox 1963d) (see Figs. 7 and 9).

The Developing Brain of the Neonate

Length-width measurements of the cerebral cortices indicate that the difference between these two measurements increases with age, where initially at birth length and width are almost equal. The most dramatic changes in the length:width ratio occur between the third and fourth weeks. Adult-like ratios appear at approximately four weeks while maturation of size to adult pro-

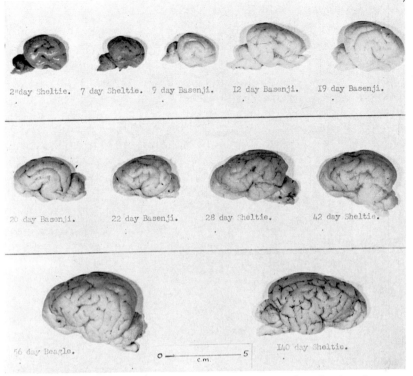

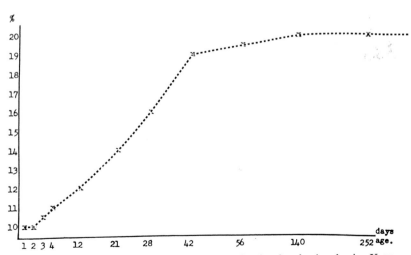

Figure 7. Postnatal development of the brain. (Note lengthening due to frontal lobe growth, & deepening of sylvian sulcus & temporal & piriform lobe enlargement with age.)

PERCENTAGE DRY MATTER IN THE DEVELOPING BRAIN.

Figure 8. Graph of perecntage dry matter in the developing brain. X = Whole brain specimen.)

portions proceeds rapidly up to six weeks of age and then more
gradually with ensuing months of development. Similarly the
percentage of dry matter of the whole brain increases rapidly up

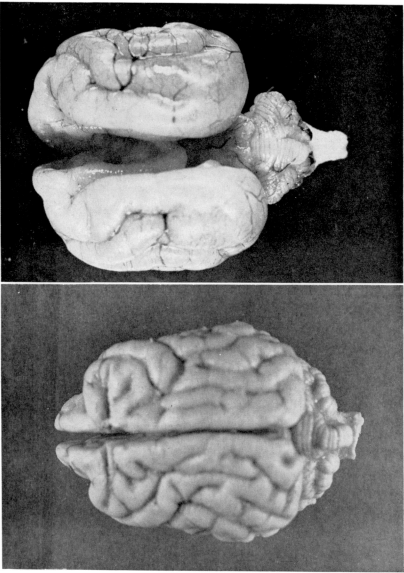

Figure 9. Comparison of newborn and adult dog brains. (Note increased
complexity of gyri & sulci enlargement of frontal and occipital
lobes in adult.)

to six weeks of age and then increases more gradually as development progresses (see Fig. 8). Normal growth weights of the whole brain indicate that development is rapid up to six weeks of age and then proceeds at a slower rate. Brain volume studies also show that a rapid increase in volume occurs up to approximately six weeks, after which time the volume falls within the adult average range.

The primary gyri and sulci are present at birth, the most marked developmental changes being the increased width of the cerebral hemispheres with concurrent deepening of the sylvian sulcus and enlargement of the temporal and piriform lobes. Increase in length is associated with great enlargement of the frontal and occipital regions with thickening and increasing complexity of gyri; at birth the frontal and occipital lobes and caudal ends of the lateral and ectolateral gyri are poorly formed (Fig. 9), but by two weeks of age the superficial features of the cerebral hemispheres resemble the adult, while mature patterns in relation to length:width ratios and relative sizes of the different lobes of the cortex are adult-like by six weeks of age. Development of the brain during the first week of life is therefore slow, but in the second and third weeks morphological changes are more rapid and correlate with behavioral and neurological changes which are also dramatic at this time and mark the onset of the critical period of socialization. The critical period of socialization reaches a peak at five to seven weeks and by twelve weeks is more or less at an end. Similarly the development of the major areas of the brain (gyrus formation and relative sizes of specific functional areas) is rapid up to six weeks of age when adult morphological characteristics are seen (Fox, 1963d & 1964c).

Studies of the cytoarchitectonics of the developing neonate dog indicate that development of the occipital cortex proceeds faster than the motor and frontal areas after birth, although all of these areas can be distinguished histologically at this time (Sarkissow, 1929). The motor cortex is the most developed area at birth. In a recent study of the postnatal development of the brain gross morphological changes in the relative sizes of different cortical areas were observed (Herre and Stephan, 1955). Histologic examination of the occipital and frontal cortices reveals that at birth

there are many primitive neuroblasts which do not become morphologically mature (complete development of dendrites and
Nissl substance formation) until approximately three weeks of
age. Cell counts indicate that as development proceeds the cerebal
cortex expands so that cell density decreases rapidly. This measurement of growth (Fig. 10) shows that there is a rapid reduction

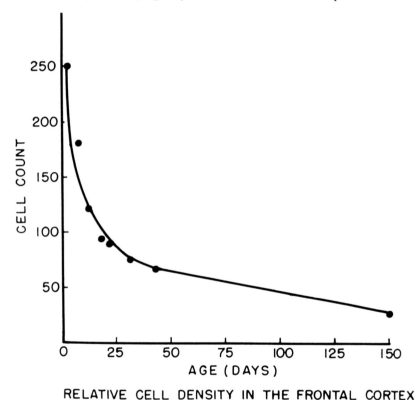

RELATIVE CELL DENSITY IN THE FRONTAL CORTEX
WITH AGE

Figure 10. Changes in cell density of the frontal cortex with age.

in cell density up to four weeks of age, by which time the cell
count is almost at the adult level. At birth, two distinct layers
of cells can be distinguished in the cortex, and by four weeks of
age, six distinct cortical layers can be recognized.

    Zolenkova and Mirtova (1960) have studied the functional
and structural peculiarities of the cerebral coretex in relation to

trauma during early development. Part of the cerebral cortex was removed in young pups and it was found that regeneration at the site of cortical extirpation occurred; the actual pattern of the gyrus was reformed. Histologic evidence for neuron reformation at the site of the lesion was uncertain, but it was remarkable that glial repair was so complete and that no obvious gyrus lesion could be found on autopsy. This finding is of interest, although more refined techniques are required to determine the regenerative potentials of the neonatal cortex. Klosovskii (1963) has also reported experiments on regeneration of the nervous system in the puppy; conditioned responses were used to aid evaluation of recovery.

Few data are available on the biochemical changes in the dog brain. Glutamic acid and glutamine levels start at a slightly higher fetal level than are present in the adult. The rise to adult values is slow and probably does not occur until more than thirty days postpartum. In contrast to this early acquisition of glutamic acid, DNA content does not reach the adult level until five months of age. The behavioral significance of this is obscure. Glutamic acid decarboxylase develops in the same pattern as GA-G (Himwich, 1962).

Mandel *et al.* (1964) studying the distribution and metabolism of ribonucleic acid found that adult levels in the C.N.S. of the dog were not reached until 5 weeks of age.

Measurements of oxygen consumption in various parts of the dog brain at different ages (Fig. 11) demonstrates the caudocephalad process of maturation of the nervous system which correlates well with reflexological studies. Between three to six weeks of age there is a rapid increase in oxygen consumption especially in the cerebral cortex and candate nucleus. By six weeks, oxygen consumption is within the adult range (Himwich and Fazekas, 1941).

Neuro-physiologic Development

The electroencephalograph of the dog shows that the alpha rhythm (an indicator of the functioning of the visual coretex) does not appear until three weeks of age, and patterns of sleep and wakefulness are indistinguishable until eighteen to twenty days. Fast activity as a definite component of the EEG of the alert

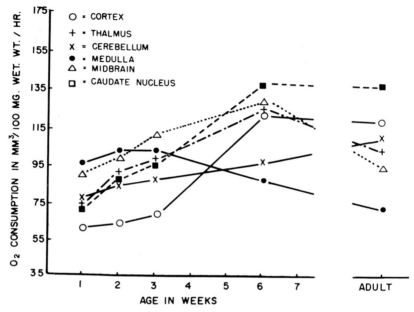

Figure 11. Oxygen consumption in different parts of the brain at different ages. (Courtesy Dr. Harold E. Himwich.)

pup is first seen at five weeks. The final adult EEG was found to develop between seven and eight weeks (Charles and Fuller, 1956). Gross changes in amplitude and frequency of these brain waves in the anaesthetized dog occur between three to four weeks, and at approximately six weeks of age the traces resemble the adult in several aspects (Fox, 1964j). Petersen and Himwich (1959) using cortical electrodes, found differences in EEG patterns during sleep and waking at one day of age and confirm Charles' and Fuller's observations in that adult patterns are not seen until after four weeks of age (Fig. 12). Pampiglione (1963) has done a similar study and found the most marked changes to occur at seven to eight days, five to six weeks and four to five months of age. Sleep patterns were first seen between three to four weeks.

As the sense organs are poorly developed at birth, what sensory afferent stimuli may the neonate dog appreciate, and to what extent does learning, or the association between afferent and efferent stimuli, i.e., responsiveness, occur in the neonate? Con-

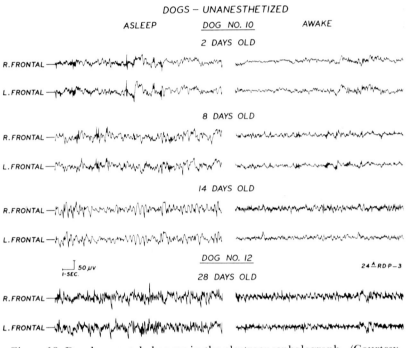

Figure 12. Developmental changes in the electroencephalograph. (Courtesy Dr. Williamina Himwich.)

ditioning experiments using tactile stimuli and mild electro-shock demonstrate that the pup is incapable of obtaining a stable response (retentive learning or stable conditioning) until approximately three weeks of age (Cornwell and Fuller, 1961). Differences in feeding ability under different experimental conditions of appetitive and aversive conditioning indicate that some learning is possible, however, in the neonate shortly after birth. (Stanley *et al.,* 1963). The reflex mechanisms concerned mainly with survival (protective, defensive, and food getting) are such that the animal must adapt rapidly to the physical environment after birth; experimentally induced changes in this environment will cause reflexly induced modifications of behavior which may or may not be interpreted as early learning.

Other Aspects of Development

The final period of neurologic development (from 28 days onwards) marks the early part of the critical period of socialization by the emergence of adult-like sensory capacities and motor abilities; primitive (neonatal) reflexes disappear as earlier behavior patterns are surpassed by more complex and independent mechanisms whereby primary social relationships can be made. Psychological changes also occur, for central inhibition of reflexes and fear responses are well developed by four weeks of age. Adult-like EEG traces appear at this time, together with very rapid development of the CNS, stability of conditioning, positive visual and auditory orientation responses, and adult-like patterns of locomotion.

Slow reflex responses during Periods I and II may be due to slow conductivity of nerve impulses, for hypomyelination is a common feature of some pathways of the peripheral nervous system of the newborn animal, while other pathways are well developed where development coincides with functional activity at birth. The facial nerve in man, for example, shows good myelination of the labial branches controlling ingestive behavior, but poor myelination of nerves controlling facial expression at birth. (Golubova, 1953). Myelination of the optic nerve in the dog was only slight during the first week but was adult-like by three weeks of age; this early hypomyelination may account for the delayed response of light stimulation (personal observations). During the period of variability to respond to auditory stimuli negative results were seen especially when the animals were feeding or awake and actively investigating the nest. In the human, similar activities may cause inhibition of the auditory startle reflex (MacKeith, 1961).

Pampiglione (1963) using EEG recordings found that the K complex (alteration in EEG trace due to afferent sensory stimuli) was seen during the first week of life with olfactory stimuli, but not until after three and one-half to four weeks did visual and auditory stimuli produce an effect on the EEG activity.

Klosovskii (1963) has studied the effects of repeated stimulation of the vestibular nerves of the dog and cat; subjects which were stimulated by rotation for short periods for several days had larger vestibular neurons than unstimulated control animals. He concludes that therapy to increase the size and function of specific receptors may be useful in cases of retarded development or prematurity.

Two primitive reflexes, namely the Magnus (or tonic neck) and crossed extensor, are not present in the adult dog or human, but in man they reappear if certain higher motor centers are damaged (DeJong, 1956). It would seem that these reflexes are inhibited by higher centers and their disappearance in the neonate dog gives an indication of the degree of maturity of the developing brain.

The behavioral significance of reflex responses may be interpreted in relation to maturational changes in the CNS and to the needs and activities of the animal modified by and adapted to a particular environment. The neonatal types of behavioral mechanisms may be linked with these reflexes where a continuum of reflexly evoked motor activity is concerned with orientation of the newborn toward thhe mother, location of the nipple, and ingestion.

When changes in the nature of the sensory and motor reflexes occur, alterations and modifications of earlier neonatal behaviour patterns also take place. Orofacial and craniocephalic responses are less stereotyped, and as feeding becomes more independent, these reflex responses weaken and eventually disappear. The importance of tactile, thermal, and geotactic orientating responses seem to become less important as audiovisual acuity improves and supersedes these more primitive mechanisms. Reflexes concerned, therefore, in orienting the animal and enabling it to find shelter and food are superseded by more advanced and independent behavior patterns.

The development of ingestive, eliminative and vocal behavior will be described in Chapter 3 and further importance will be laid upon the effects of early experience modifying later behavior in these behavior patterns.

Overt behavior is restricted by an animal's sensory and locomotor capacities; the emergence of new capacities allow the onset of new types of behavior. By understanding normal neuro-physiologic and biochemical changes occurring during development, we may discover more periods or phases in which, during development, rapid changes occur prior to behavioral change.

Other aspects of development should also be understood. Behavior of the neonate is such that et-epimelesis (care seeking) and certain reflexes (rooting and auriculonasocephalic) maintain the pup close to the mother for environmental temperature has a direct effect on the behavior of pups (Fredericson *et al.*, 1956). This is important for at birth the pup is poikilothermic, and body temperature is maintained by thermal conductance from the mother and other litter mates. Temperature control (using hot and cold room tests) is poorly developed until three weeks of age. Weak shivering is first seen at three days, but in a cold room the isolated pup experiences a severe fall in temperature with decreased heart rate. This marked drop in temperature is seen during the first ten days of life, after which follows a transition from ten to fourteen days where body temperature does not fall so rapidly and decrease in heart rate is less. Good temperature control is seen from eighteen to twenty days onward, with slight increase in heart rate as in the adult. When exposed to an elevated temperature, panting and increased respiration is ineffective in maintaining body temperature until three weeks. Prior to this time, there is a decrease in heart rate in the newborn as temperature increases (Jensen and Ederstorm, 1955). Apparently the vagus nerve does not have an effect on the heart of the newborn dog (Saltmann, 1877).

This leads us to the problem of the development of physiological-emotional reactions, for the heart rate is a sensitive physiologic index reflecting reactions to a variety of psycho-physiologic factors. Heart rate increases during the first week after birth but at two to three weeks there is an abrupt decline in heart rate which remains low in the third through fifth weeks and then rises again to a level almost as high as the initial point. After this there is a slow decline toward the adult level. This early decline in rate coincides with the period of socialization and probably represents an emotional reaction to handling during auscultation. Once socialization is complete, this reaction disappears. On the other hand, it is possible that the change at seven weeks represents a more complete physiologic control (vagus) over the heart rate (Scott, 1963).

Using cardiac conditioning techniques, similar results to motor conditioning were obtained, in that conditioning was unstable until after four weeks of age, which may mark the onset of the ability to associate stimuli and develop learned responses (Fuller and Christake, 1959).

Conditioned Reflex Studies

Russian work on the development of behavior in the dog has been studied especially with Pavlovian conditioning techniques. Autonomic (respiration and heart rate) responses were correlated with age (Volokhov et al., 1959). It was found that the autonomic components precede motor ones in the development of orientation reactions to sound stimuli. A bell was used as the conditioning stimulus and a mild electrical shock was the unconditioned stimulus. In older dogs, changes in heart rate and respiration and motor orientation were seen concurrently on the first stimulation. Heart and respiration slowed in younger animals prior to investigatory activity while these autonomic components increased in older dogs. Between sixteen to eighteen days of age there was a marked increase in heart rate and respiration. Changes in passive defensive and investigatory reflexes have been studied (Mirzakarimova et al., 1958), and were found to occur between thirty to forty-five days (investigatory reflexes) and three to four months onwards (passive defensive), where maximal intensity was found at these respective ages. These responses may be ethologically interpreted as approach and avoidance behavior and these data support the critical period of socialization hypothesis where approximately five to seven weeks is the peak for approach behavior (and therefore socialization with man) and twelve weeks of age onwards the peak for avoidance behavior, after which time socialization is difficult to establish (Freedman et al., 1961).

Cardiac conditioning (to sound buzzer and heat or cold stimuli) was found to be quickly established in young pups but was unstable. Differentiation was elaborated with difficulty and remained unstable for a long time, indicating weakness of processes of internal inhibition of the cortex of young animals (Ovakimyan, 1961).

Klyavina et al. (1958) have studied the conditioned responses of pups tested at fifteen and thirty days of age; sound followed by food reward or electric shock were used as stimuli. At thirty days of age the results were the same as in four month old dogs. Stable conditioning was obtained after less than ten trials. At fifteen days, more trials to form the conditioned reflex with food reward were required, approximately forty pairings to produce stability. With electric shock, eighteen trials and eighty pairings were required to produce stable responses at this age. The results agree with Cornwell and Fuller (1961) in showing that there is a marked change in the ability to form conditioned responses between fifteen to thirty days of age. Also, this ability is developed more rapidly in association with feeding than with electric shock. Although hearing is poorly developed at fifteen days of age, it is clear that prior to three weeks of age more experience is required before stable associations are formed and retained.

The Visual System

The visual system, examined by electro-retinography, and histologic and reflexologic techniques, undergoes gradual maturation after birth (Parry, 1953) which has been well described.

Reflexological studies show that, although the eyelids are closed until approximately two weeks of age, weak photomotor responses may be elicited shortly after birth. The emergence of positive visual orientation prior to visual fixation may indicate that visual orientation is governed primarily by subcortical centers. The emergence of the menace reaction, visual fixation, and depth discrimination (visual cliff test) at four weeks of age would seem to indicate that it is not until this time that higher cortical activities are present. These sudden changes at four weeks of age follow a transition period from fourteen days of age, when all other ocular reflexes are demonstrable (Fox, 1963g). This transition period resembles visual (objective) agnosia seen in adult dogs affected with intracranial neoplasia.

Correlated with these reflexological studies are cellular changes in the occipital cortex; adult-like characteristics are seen at four weeks of age. Earlier work has demonstrated that the occipital cortex of the dog develops more rapidly than other cortical areas after birth (Sarkissow, 1929). Embryonic structures, including hyaloid artery remnants, pupillary membranes, radii lentis and corpora nigra lentis have been observed in young pups, and also pupillary spasm (resembling "hippus"), ocular hyperkinesias, and convergent strabismus (Fox, 1963g).

Electroretinography shows that the retina is poorly functional until five to six weeks of age, when visual responses are adult-like in all characteristics (Parry, 1953).

Response of the Immature to Disease

Finally, one must consider the reactions of the newborn to disease. The blood brain barrier is apparently impervious to bilirubin and toluidine blue (Himwich, 1963), but experimentally induced toxemias (staphylococcus and dysenteric toxins) have produced interesting clinical findings that throw some light on the functional activity of the brain at different ages (Korniyenko, 1958). When the toxin is given to eighteen to twenty day old pups a lethal dose causes a protracted collapse with respiratory and cardiac slowing, fall in body temperature (indicative of diencephalic heat regulation centre damage) and disappearance of cortical electrical activity. There is therefore inactivation of cortical centres although the bulbar regions maintaining respiration and heart rate continue to function but at a weakening level for some hours. This dissociation of different functioning levels of the CNS was only seen in early stages of growth after twenty days of age and was no longer seen at two to three months, when a lethal dose of toxin caused sudden collapse due to almost simultaneous cessation of function of all the different levels of the nervous system. Similar symptoms have been attributed to canine viral hepatitis and streptococci causing a "fading" syndrome (Davies and Skulski, 1956). This phenomenon of immature reaction to noxious agents has been studied where no infectious agents were isolated; pups died from hypothermia due to multiple factors (cold exposure, maternal neglect and malnutrition) and similar clinical symptoms were seen. There was protracted collapse, slowing of respiration and heart rate, and periodic apnoea terminating in a syndrome of cardiopulmonary failure and arrest (Fox, 1963h).

With such knowledge of development, the indices of normality may be applied clinically to congenital or developmental anomalies or experimentally to induced morphologic or behavioral abnormalities. Psycho-social problems in many may be experimentally investigated in animals (see Chapter 5) applying a basic understanding of the neuro-endocrine and psycho-physiological mechanisms of animals.

References

Charles, M. S. and Fuller, J. L.: Developmental study of the electroencephalogram of the dog. *Electroenceph. Clin. Neurophysiol., 8*:645-652, 1956.

Collias, N. E.: The development of social behavior in birds. *Auk, 69*:127-159, 1952.

Cornwell, A. C. and Fuller, J. L.: Conditioned responses in young puppies. *J. Comp. Physiol, Psychol., 54*:13-15, 1961.

Davies, M. E. and Skulski, G.: A study of beta-hemolytic streptococci in the fading puppy in relation to canine virus hepatitis infection in the dam. *Brit. Vet. J., 112*:404-416, 1956.

DeJong, R.: *The Neorologic Examination.* New York, Cassell Co., 1956.

Fox, M. W.: Reflexes and innate behavioural mechanisms in the neonate dog. *J. Small Anim. Pract., 4*:85-99, 1963a.

Fox, M. W.: The development and significance of muscle tone and posture in the neonate dog. *Amer. J. Vet. Res., 24*:103:1232-1238, 1963b.

Fox, M. W.: Development and clinical significance of superficial reflexes in the dog. *Vet. Rec., 75*:14:378-383, 1963c.

Fox, M. W.: Gross morphology and development of the canine brain. *Amer. J. Vet. Res., 24*:103:1240-1247, 1963d.

Fox, M. W.: The ontogeny of behavior and neurologic responses in the dog. *Animal Behavior, 12*:301-311, 1964e.

Fox, M. W.: Behavioral correlates of myelinization of the spinal cord of the dog. Unpublished data, 1964f.

Fox, M. W.: Postnatal ontogeny of the canine eye. *J. Am. Vet. M.A., 1943*:9:968-975, 1963g.

Fox, M. W.: Observations on neonatal mortality in the dog. *J. Am. Vet. M.A., 143*:1219-1223, 1963h.

Fox, M. W.: The effects of barbiturate anesthesia on the developing EEG of the dog. *Vet. Rec. 76*:768-70, 1964i.

Fox, M. W.: The postnatal growth of the canine brain and correlated anatomical and behavioral changes during neuro-ontogenesis *Growth, 28*:135-141, 1964j.

Fredericson, E., Gurney, N. and Dubuis, E.: Relationship between environmental temperature and behavior of puppies. *J. Comp. Physiol. Psychol., 49*:278, 1956.

Freedman, D. G., Elliot, E. and King, J. A.: Critical period in the social development of dogs. *Science, 133*:1016-17, 1961.

Fuller, J. L. and Christake, A.: Conditioning of leg flexion and cardio-acceleration in the puppy. *Fed. Proc., 18*:1:49, 1959.

Gessell, A.: *The Embryology of Behavior.* New York, Harper, 1945.

Golubova, E. L.: Physiology and pathology of the nervous system in animals and man in the early stages of development (Conference). *Pavlov J. Higher Nerv. Activity, 8*:5, 728-734, 1958.

Harman, J.: Cited personal communication by Scott, J. P.: The Process of primary socialization in canine and human infants. *Monogr. Soc. Res.*

Child. Develop., No. *85*:28:1, 15, 1963.

Herre, W. and Stephan, H.: Zur postnatalen morphogenese des hirnes verschiedener haushundsrassen. *Gegenbauers Morph. Jahrb., 96*:210-264, 1955.

Hess, E. S.: Imprinting in animals. *Sci. Amer., 198*:3:81-90, 1958.

Himwich, W.: Biochemical and neurophysiological development of the brain in the neonatal period. *Int. Rev. Neurobiol., 4*:117-158, 1962.

Himwich, H. E. and Fazekas, J. F.: Comparative studies of the metabolism of the brain of infant and adult dogs. *Am. J. Physiol., 132*:454, 1941.

Ingram, T. T. S.: Changes in muscle tone in infancy. *Cereb. Palsy Bull., 5*:6, 1959.

James, W. T.: Behavior of newborn pups. *J. Comp. Physiol. Psychol., 45*:329, 1952.

Jensen, C. and Ederstrom, H. E.: Development of temperature regulation in the dog. *Amer. J. Physiol., 183*:340-343, 1955.

Klosovskii, B. N.: *The Development of the Brain and its Disturbance by Harmful Factors.* New York, Macmillan Co., Pergammon Press, 1963.

Klyavina, M. P., Kobakova, E. M., Stelmak, L. N. and Troshikhin, V. A.: On the speed of formation of conditioned reflexes in dogs in ontogenesis. *Pavlov J. Higher Nerv. Activity, 8*:929-936, 1958.

Kobayashi, T., Inman, O., Buno, W. and Himwich, H. E.: A multidisciplinary study of changes in mouse brain with age. *Recent Adv. Biol. Psychiatry 5*:293-308, 1963, New York, Plenum Press, Inc.

Korniyenko, I. A.: Physiology and pathology of the central nervous system in animals and man in the early stages of development (Conference). *Pavlov J. Higher Nerv. Activity, 8*:5, 728-734, 1958.

Langworthy, O. R.: Development of behavior and myelinization of the nervous system in the human fetus and infant. *Contr. Embryol. Carn. Inst., 24*:1-57, 1933.

Lorenz, K.: Der Kumpan in der Umvelt des Vogels. *J. Ornithol., 83*:137-213, 289-413, 1935.

MacKeith, R. C.: Anencephaly and somatic stability. Cited in discussion, *Ciba Symposium Somatic Stability of the Newly Born,* Little, Brown & Co., 1961, p. 288.

Mandel P., *et al.*: Distribution and metabolism of ribonucleic acid in the vertebrate central nervous system. Page 149-163 in *Comparative Neurochemistry,* ed., D. Richter, Pergammon Press. New York, MacMillan, 1964.

Mirzakamirova, M. G., Stelmakh, L. N. and Troshikhin, V. A.: Directed changes in passive-defensive and investigatory reflexes in ontogenesis. *Palov, J. Higher Nerv. Activity, 8*:5, 1958.

Ovakimyan, R. R.: Vascular conditioned reflexes in pups. *Palov J. Higher Nerv. Activity, 11*:3, 1961.

Pampiglione, G.: *Development of Cerebral Function in the Dog.* London, Butterworths, 1963.

Parry, H. B.: Structure and development of the retina of the normal dog.

Brit. J. Ophthal., 38:295, 1953.

Petersen, J. C. and Hiwich, W. A.: Development of the EEG in the dog. *The Physiologist,* 2:93, 1959.

Saltmann, O.: *Jahrb. Kinderheilk., 11*:107, 1877. Cited by Jensen & Ederstorm in *Am. J. Physiol., 183*:340-343, 1955.

Sarkissow, S.: Über die postnatale entwicklung ein zeiner cytoarchitektonisher felder beim hunde. *J. Psychol. u. Neurol., 39*:4, 6, 486-505, 1929.

Scott, J. P.: Critical periods in the development of social behavior in puppies. *Psychosom. Med., 20*:42-45, 1958.

Scott, J. P.: Critical periods in behavioral development. *Science, 138*:949-958, 1962.

Scott, J. P.: The process of primary socialization in canine and human infants. *Monogr. Soc. Res. Child Develop., 85*:28:1, 1963.

Stanley, W. C., Cornwell, A. C., Poggiani, C. and Trattner, A.: Conditioning in the neonate puppy. *J. Comp. Physiol. Psychol., 56*:211-214, 1963.

Thomas, A.: *Equilibre et Equilibration.* Paris, Masson, 1940.

Thomas A., Chesni, Y. and Dargessies, S.: The neurological examination of the infant. *Little Club Dev. Med., 1,* 1961.

Volokhov, A. A., Nikitina, G. M. and Novikova, E. G.: Development of vegetative components in the orientation and defensive conditioned reflexes during ontogenesis. *Pavlov J. Higher Nerv. Activity, 9*:3, 1959.

Williams, E. and Scott, J. P.: The development of social behavior patterns in the mouse in relation to natural periods. *Behavior, 6*:1:35-64, 1953.

Zolenkova, E. G. and Mirtova, L. M.: Functional and structural peculiarities of the cerebral cortex in relation to trauma during ontogenetic development. Pavlov. J. Higher Nervous Activity, *10*:1:118-128, 1960h.

Chapter 3

NORMAL BEHAVIOR PATTERNS OF THE ADULT DOG

USING THE CLASSIFICATION of behavior patterns as described by Scott (1962) as organized segments of behavior having specific functions, we shall discuss the following systems of behavior; ingestive, eliminative, sexual, care-giving (epimeletic), care-soliciting (et-epimeletic), agonistic, allelomimetic, shelter seeking, and investigatory behavior.

Sexual Behavior

The onset of sexual activity varies between breeds and individuals of these breeds. The chow dog, for example, does not breed until it is much older than the female, while the beagle dog will breed some months before the female; the basenji bitch has only one annual estrus cycle, although the photoperiodicity of the cycle may be altered experimentally (Fuller, 1956). False heats resembling pro-estrus may occur three months before the first heat cycle in the young bitch (Whitney, 1947). No clearly defined seasonal incidence of estrus has been found in the dog (Engle, 1946).

Sexual activities, mounting, clasping, and pelvic thrusts, are seen normally from four to seven weeks of age more in male puppies at play than in females (Rheingold, 1963). Active courtship occurs when the female first comes into estrus; the male, although the gonads may be functional, tends to mate at an organically later age, suggesting some psychological differences between the sexes. Olfaction in the male is an important primary receptor governing the onset of sexual behavior; the urine of the bitch in heat is a very positive stimulus (Beach and Gilmore, 1949). Other sensory receptors are of less importance, for totally blind and deaf dogs have been known to breed and rear offspring normally. A bitch spayed at any age is rendered sexually nonreceptive, while the male is nonresponsive only if castration is performed before puberty (Beach, 1950). Courtship, mating behavior and intensity of sexual activity have been well recorded by Fuller and Dubuis (1962).

Environmental factors especially influence sexual behavior in the male; familiarity of surroundings and handler are often essential if a stud dog is to consummate sexual activity. So it is a good rule to bring the bitch into the male's quarters for mating. Occasionally the male may not be dominant enough during the courtship and the bitch frequently mounts the sire and stimulates his aggressive behavior. There are many reports of males and females reared together and the female is the dominant animal in the social hierarchy, mating under such circumstances is rare, although the bitch may mate with a dominant strange male (Scott, 1961). Hormonal induction of estrus using, P.M.S. and L.H. is easily obtained although treated bitches show all the signs of estrus, they will not breed. This behavioral deficit is not fully understood. Better control of estrus has been achieved with synthetic progesterones; the drug is given when the first signs of estrus are seen and estrus is suspended if the drug is then given daily. Upon withdrawal of treatment, normal estrus is resumed and breeding with the production of normal offspring follows (Jochle, 1963). By this method, controlled breeding and regular production may be ensured in a large dog colony.

Homosexuality, more in young males than females, and masturbation are traits frequently observed during play in groups of young dogs housed together, and in the house pet who may also assume sexual postures over inanimate objects. Such behavior is within the normal range of sexual activity in the dog.

Maternal or Epimeletic behavior during parturition normally follows an efficient sequence of events (Harrop, 1960; Bleicher, 1962). Nestmaking may occur toward the onset of parturition. The presence of a familiar human handler during parturition and prepartum familiarization to the whelping environment greatly reduce postnatal mortalities. Normally, dying puppies—in a state of hypothermic lethargy—are pushed outside the nest or buried by the bitch in spite of their distress vocalization.

Rheingold (1963) gives an excellent account of maternal activities including nursing, weaning and post-weaning social behavior. Following parturition, the bitch tends to the litter and stays with it until approximately three weeks, when the number of daily contacts begin to decrease. This marks the onset of weaning and the gradual cessation of nursing activities. Food regurgitation for the litter, and both play and herding of offspring, have been seen after this time. Food regurgitation may be a normal material mechanism of introducing the pups to solid food (Martins, 1949). Punishing and avoiding contact with the pups (separating activities) also begin to appear when the litter is three to four weeks of age.

During nursing, the bitch will ingest the urine and feces of the pup, elimination being reflexively stimulated by the bitch licking the ano-genital regions. The nest is therefore kept clean. Normally this cleaning behavior disappears at approximately four weeks, when the pups begin to leave the nest and eliminate independently. Retrieving of stray pups is frequently achieved by licking the face of the pup so that the pup would orientate and then crawl in the direction of the stimulus (rooting reflex). Carrying stray pups in the mouth was rarely seen. The sight of the moving pup and not its vocalizations during parturition, or at a later age when strayed from the litter, stimulates the bitch to retrieve it (Bleicher, 1962; Rheingold, 1963). In pseudopregnancy, nest making activities, lactation, and even first stage labor may be seen, together with displaced maternal protection of inanimate objects placed in the nest, are common phenomena and tend to be recurrent. Such abortive behavioral activities cannot be regarded as entirely normal, for the house dog is frequently not allowed to breed for several heat cycles, if at all. Ovariohysterectomy is obviously indicated in severe recurrent cases.

There are definite breed tendencies towards false pregnancy; maiden beagles, for example, seldom show symptoms of pseudopregnancy following estrus (Anderson and Wooten, 1959).

Et-epimeletic (Care-seeking) Behavior

During the period of nursing, reflexes and innate behavioral mechanisms are such that the neonate maintains maximal contact with the dam. Also, interactions between litter-mates change during development, as shelter seeking necessity is of decreasing importance as somatic stability and homeothermy develop. Rheingold (1963) observed that up to one week of age the pups burrow over each other to form a heap, maximal contact aiding thermal conductance and maintenance of euthermia. At two weeks of age, behavior changes; there is less heaping, and pups tend to lie parallel to each other. By four weeks of age they sleep in small groups and at six weeks they sleep alone. Et-epimeletic vocalization is discussed elsewhere in this chapter under "Communication." Distress vocalization in young pups exposed to different environmental conditions (isolation and strangeness) has been studied, and vocalization is a good indicator of emotional arousal (Elliot and Scott, 1961).

Eliminative Behavior

Urination and defecation are important means of communication in the dog for both social (territorial marking) and sexual activities (Beach and Gillmore, 1949). Raising of the hind leg prior to urination in the male is hormonally controlled and is not a learned activity mimicked from other dogs. Normal leg raising occurs during puberty in the male but may be hormonally induced at thirty-nine days of age if testosterone is given (Martins and Valle, 1948) to the male or early in life to female pups. Hormones in this case have a direct effect on behavior.

Olfactory cues are important in the sexual attraction of male to female dogs, and experiments with males presented with the diluted urine of females have shown that the male can discriminate between the urine of estrus and non-estrus females, even when the urine sample has been greatly diluted. This may indicate that there are special substances in the urine of the estrus female (pheromones); they may also be in the urine of feminized males with testicular tumors, for male dogs are also attracted to these animals. Gier (1954) has studied the effects of chlorophyll derivatives on mating odors, and it is possible that these substances mask the specific attraction factor in the urine, for treated females do not attract males during estrus. Sick male dogs frequently squat and urinate in the female position. Under severe emotional stress, anxiety, or forced restraint, urination and defecation may follow, and evacuation of the anal glands. Submissive urination will be described later in this book (Chapter 7).

Ingestive Behavior

Sucking in the new born gradually increases in efficiency in the first three days after birth and the fore limbs are used to push the breast—probably to keep the breast out of the face of the pup and allow easier respiration. At seventeen days when the pups are stronger and more active, forelimb thrusting is no longer seen. Orienting reflexes concerned with feeding have been discussed in Chapter 2. At approximately three weeks of age a new sucking pattern appears. Sucking is no longer rhythmic but becomes noisy and sporadic, perhaps indicative of an intermittent flow of milk. Non-nutritive sucking on the bodies of other pups may occur as a result of inadequate nursing, or hunger, but such displacement activity may alleviate an "oral tension" in these pups. Non-nutritive sucking may occur in satiated pups though, and it may be in these cases that the activity itself is self-rewarding and self-reinforcing (Ross et al., 1957). Also at three weeks of age, solid food may be taken from the mother's feed bowl, or the litter may eat the vomitus of the bitch if she develops regurgitation activities at the time of weaning. Exploratory oral behavior appears at the onset of the critical period of socialization; pups will chew, lick and investigate small objects in the pen and may ingest such objects. Coprophagy is also seen during this period.

In group feeding experiments it has been found that pups tend to eat more than if fed singly (Ross and Ross, 1949). This competitive phenomenon of "social facilitation" does not persist, however, for when dominant-subordinate relations are established at the food bowl, the subordinate pup may be inadequately nourished (James, 1949).

There are several studies on ingestive behavior in the adult dog. It has been shown that the dog regulates its food intake largely according to the calorie content, and dilution with non-nutrient

bulk materials has only a temporary influence on total intake
(Mayer, 1953). Factors influencing water intake have been
studied by Adolph (1943).

Agonistic Behavior

Play fighting is first seen in the litter at four to five weeks of
age, and such competition leads to a social hierarchy being established which may remain stable for many years (Fig. 1). Lorenz

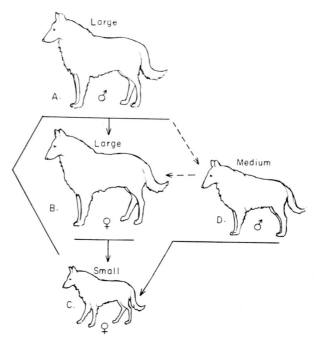

DOMINANCE RELATIONSHIPS IN A LITTER OF ONE-YEAR-OLD SHELTIES

Figure 1. Dominance hierarchy in a litter of dogs.

(1952) has given detailed descriptive accounts of dominant and
submissive behavior characteristics of both wolves and dogs while
Pawlowski and Scott (1956) have studied experimentally the
effects of heredity in the development of dominance. Breed differences in the rigidity of the order of this behavioral organization
exist, sex being an important factor in some breeds, but not in
others (King, 1954).

In general, strange dogs when introduced to a closed social group (i.e., a group in which the social order of dominance is fixed) of the same breed, were attacked and rejected more than dogs of a different breed. This discrimination against strangers similar to the group in sex and breed may be because the group members recognized strangers similar to the other individual members of the group. Since the group members formed a social hierarchy by aggressive behavior they were conditioned to react aggressively toward their own breed, and not to the same degree toward strange dogs of another breed (King, 1954). Beagles are typically less competitive and sex is of less importance; dogs selected for working in packs, i.e., hunting dogs, would necessary be of this latter type. The domestic dog also establishes a hierarchical relationship with man; normally man is the dominant individual, for regular handling of the puppy acts as a form of dominance over the dog. Shaking by the scruff is a recognized means of gaining complete dominance over an animal without inflicting further trauma or pain. Indeed, painful corrective treatment increases agression for pain is associated especially with fighting. Abnormalities in social behavior will be delt with further on in this paper. Territorial defense is one of the most immediate causes of aggression if the dog's territory is violated by a strange dog or human. Such behavior can be avoided by rearing the young dog under submission with the owner actively dominant and socializing the animal to a wide variety of both human and canine neighbors. Severe aggression or avoidance behavior and fear biting on its home territory are characteristic of the socially maladjusted dog. Tying up a dog may increase aggression and the great tendency for a dog to fight while on the leash is probably due to agonistic territorial defense. Any sudden change in social environment may disrupt the routine behavior pattern of the animal and lead to unexpected and unpredicted agonistic behavior. (Worden, 1954). A dog may be trained to be aggressive, but genetic factors are also involved in the selection of certain strains to fulfill particular tasks.

Redding *et al.* (1964) have described a phenomenon of alternate sleep and wakefulness; some dogs showed periodic EEG changes indicative of phasic changes in sleep. They suggest that this may once have been of survival value, protecting the dog from predators.

Allelomimetic Behavior

Allelomimetic behavior, or group coordinated activity (Scott, 1958), is seen especially in young puppies which will follow each other or as when a puppy follows a human being. In the adult dog such behavior is seen in the dog pack, either hunting or free-roaming house dogs trailing a female in estrus. Fighting under these circumstances is rare. Social facilitation occurs during each activity, e.g., dogs run in pairs run faster (Vogel et al., 1950); the motivation underlying this behavior has not been explained; perhaps it is one of communication facilitating group activities, e.g., pack hunting. Pups reared in isolation up to the age of sixteen weeks make few body contacts with each other (Fuller, personal communication), indicating experiential deficit reduces social interactions and allelomimetic activities.

Communication

Besides scent post and urination activities, dogs communicate in other ways. Posture—attitudes of threat, aggression, or submission determined by head and body carriage, tail posture and pilo-erection; submissive paw raising, prostration, and urination are common communicatory activities (Lorenz, 1952). Vocalization is another important means of communication, having great breed variations. In the neonate, distress vocalizations (and care seeking et-epimeletic activities) may be important in maintaining maternal attention.

Rheingold (1963) has observed the developmental changes of vocalization. At birth, non-protest murmurs (mewing, clicking noises) are emitted by the pups, reaching a peak at four to nine days and disappearing at five weeks. Whimpers (protests) reach a peak at seven to nine days and disappear at four weeks, while yelps persist. Grunts and barking are not present at birth but appear at approximately three weeks of age, reaching a peak at nine weeks of age and persisting.

In the adult, aggressive growling, submissive whining, territorial defensive barking, and the bay of the hunting dog are vocal activities expressing or reinforcing behavior of the individual which is communicated to others. Sound spectograph analysis of breed differences in vocalization is providing further interesting data on vocal communication in the dog (Scott, 1961).

Salzinger *et al.* (1962) have studied conditioning of vocalization in the dog and find that operant conditioning techniques can be applied to vocalization, modifying unconditioned vocal behavior. They conclude that the fact that vocal behavior of animals can be modified by means of operant reinforcement makes it appear that it possibly constitutes an evolutionary precursor of verbal behavior in the human species.

Estrogen given to adult male dogs eventually reduces or suppresses spirited barking (Lienert and Mathois, 1955). This hormonal effect may actually suppress the A.D.R. (active defensive reflex) to the strength of the female counterpart of the male, and therefore reduce aggressive or territorial-defensive barking.

References

Adolph, E. F.: *Physiological Regulation*. Lancaster, Cattell, 1943.

Anderson, A. C. and Wooten, E.: Estrus cycle in the dog, in *Reproduction in Domestic Animals*. H. H. Cole and P. T. Cupps, eds. New York, Academic Press, 1959.

Beach, F. A. and Gilmore, R. W.: Response of male dogs to urine from females in heat. *J. Mammal., 30:*391-392, 1949.

Beach, F. A.: Sexual behavior in animals and man. *The Harvey Lectures, Series 43:*254-280. Springfield, Ill., Thomas, 1950.

Bleicher, N.: Behavior of the bitch during parturition. *J. Am. Vet. M. A., 140:*1076-1082, 1962.

Elliot, G. and Scott, J. P.: The development of emotional distress reactions to separation in puppies. *J. Genet. Psychol., 99:*3-22, 1961.

Engle, E. T.: No seasonal breeding cycle in the dog. *J. Mammal., 27:*79-81, 1946.

Fuller, J. L.: Photoperiodic control of estrus in the Basenji. *J. Hered., 47:*179-180, 1956.

Fuller, J. L. and DuBuis, E.: The behavior of dogs. Chapter 15 in *The Behavior of Domestic Animals*, E. S. E. Hafez, ed., London, Balliere, Tindall & Cox, 1962.

Gier, H. T.: Effect of cholorophyll derivatives on mating odors of dogs. *Vet. Med., 49:*377-380, 391, 1954.

Harrop, A. E.: *Reproduction in the Dog*. Baltimore, Williams & Wilkins Co., 1960.

James, W. T.: Dominant and submissive behavior in puppies as indicative by food intake. *J. Genet. Psychol., 75:*33-34, 1949.

Jochle, W.: Personal communication, Fecunda A. G., Aarau, Switzerland, 1963.

King, J. A.: Closed social groups among domestic animals. *Proc. Amer. Philos. Soc., 93*:327-336, 1954.

Lienert, E., & Mathois, H.: Experiments on the supression of spirited barking of male dogs by means of estrogen. *Wiener, Tierarztl, Monatsschr., 42*: 100-107, 1955.

Lorenz, K.: *King Solomon's Ring.* New York, Crowell, 1952.

Martins, T.: Disgorging of food to the puppies by the lactating dog. *Physiol. Zoöl., 22*:169-172, 1949.

Martins, T. and Valle, J. F.: Hormonal regulation of the micturition behavior of the dog. *J. Comp. Physiol. Psychol., 41*:301-311, 1948.

Mayer, J.: Caloric requirements and obesity in dogs. *Gaines Veterinary Symposium,* New York, 1953.

Pawlowski, A. A. and Scott, J. P.: Hereditary differences in the development of dominance in a litter of puppies. *J. comp. physiol. Psychol., 49*: 353-358, 1956.

Redding, R. W., Prynn B. & Colwell, R. K.: The phenomenon of alternate sleep and wakefulness in the dog. *J. Amer. Vet. M. A., 144*:6, 605-6, 1964.

Rheingold, H. L.: Maternal behavior in the dog. Chapter 5 in *Maternal Behavior in Mammals,* H. L. Rheingold, ed. New York, John Wiley and Sons, Inc., 1963.

Ross, S., Fisher, A. E. and King, O.: Sucking behavior; a review of the literature. *J. Genet. Psychol., 91*:63-81, 1957.

Ross, S. and Ross, J.: Social facilitation of feeding behavior in dogs. 1. Group and solitary feeding. *J. Genet. Psychol., 74*:97-108, 1949.

Salzinger F. and Waller, M. B.: The operant control of vocalization in the dog. *J. Exp. Anal. Behav., 53*:383-389, 1962.

Scott, J. P.: *Animal Behavior.* Chicago, Univ. of Chicago Press, 1858.

Scott, J. P.: Sound spectrograph analysis of dog vocalization. *Amer. Zoöl., 1*:387, 1961.

Scott, J. P.: Animal sexuality. In *Encyclopedia of Sexual Behavior,* A. E. Ellis and A. Abarbenel, eds., New York, Hawthorn, 1961.

Scott, J. P.: Introduction to animal behavior. Chapter 1 in *The Behaviour of Domestic Animals,* E. S. E. Hafez, ed., London, Balliere Tindall & Cox, 1962.

Vogel, H. H., Scott, J. P. and Marston, M. V.: Social facilitation and allelomemetic behavior in dogs. 1. Social Facilitation in a non-competitive situation. *Behavior, 2*:121-134, 1950.

Whitney, L. F.: *How to Breed Dogs.* Rev. ed., New York, Orange Judd, 1947.

Worden, A. N.: Abnormal behavior in the dog and cat. *Vet. Rec., 71*:966-981, 1959.

Chapter 4

INHERITANCE AND BEHAVIOR

Breed Selection

SELECTIVE BREEDING has given rise to a large variety of dogs, each breed having distinct physical and behavioral characteristics. Certain behavior traits and physical features have been intensified in some breeds, while other characteristics have been reduced or eliminated, so that the particular breed may perform a specific function. Herding and droving abilities are predominant in sheepdogs, and selective breeding has produced strains that are easily trained to perform these tasks. Strong physique and aggressive territorial defensive behavior have been combined to give guard dogs and police dogs such as the doberman and the German shepherd. A greater variety of hunting dogs have been selected to perform to an optimum some specific activity. By virtue of their fine physique, great speed and well developed eyesight, the saluki greyhound and whippet are used for hunting small game, while heavier breeds which also hunt "by eye" include the Irish wolfhound and Scottish deerhound. Intermediate breeds, slightly smaller and that hunt by eye, include the spaniels, setters, pointers and retrievers, which are used especially for bird hunting. The hound breeds, notably the bloodhound, foxhound and beagle, have been selected to hunt by scent. Smaller breeds for flushing out vermin were developed for maximal aggression and physique appropriate for the size of their prey. The daschund was selected for badger hunting and the fox terriers for fox and small vermin eradication.

Selection of certain traits from different breeds have been combined to produce new varieties, which are established as new

49

breeds if these combinations produce the desired effect. Many modern breeds have been selected in this way from foundation-stock of hound, terrier and hunting dog.

For more specialized tasks, involving complex training from an early age, the retrievers and German Shepherds have been selected as probably the best dogs to serve as guide for blind people (Pfaffenberger, 1963).

Heredity of Traits and Environmental Effects and Training

The inheritance of behavior and temperament is complex, for the characteristics of a breed comprise a combination of several independently inherited traits which are modified by genetic factors (Scott, 1954). No trait is inherited as such; genetic factors are transmitted by inheritance, but the traits themselves are modified by interacting genetic and environmental factors. Training and early experience greatly influence these traits, and it is the selection of traits which facilitate easier training to perform particular tasks that differentiates one breed from another, and individuals within the breed.

Fuller (1955) has studied the hereditary differences in trainability of purebred dogs, and concludes that highly specific behavior traits are involved in breed differences and that particulate measures of behavior which fit the particulate concepts of genetics would be more useful in the understanding of the inheritance of behavior than by employing measurements of constitutional types.

The genetics of trainability, heredity and aggression have been studied extensively and will be briefly discussed (Whitney, 1932). It is not within the scope of this book to consider the training of specially selected breeds to perform particular tasks. The training of gun dogs and guide dogs for the blind has been well described by professional trainers (Pfaffenberger, 1947 and 1963; Saunders, 1952).

Another important use of dogs is for companionship, and a great variety, differing widely in size and shape, have been produced. A physically small, easily dominated and controlled dog is the most popular type, having expressive affection-seeking behavior toward the owner and a mild degree of territorial defensive behavior in that it will bark when strangers are near.

There is therefore a selected series of dogs that covers the whole spectrum of behavior, each breed having certain selected characteristics that enable it to perform maximally a certain behavior pattern, e.g., scent trailing in hounds, while other behavior traits are reduced, e.g., agression and fighting in hounds.

Behavior genetics is an important field of research (see Chapter 5) and the dog has been used extensively in these studies (Fuller and Thompson, 1960; Fuller and Scott, 1954). Genes may modify anatomical, metabolic and endocrine systems, and their effect is expressed in the behavior of the animal. A monumental study by Stockard et al. (1941) who crossbred various breed types, ranging from the achondroplastic dachshund, the brachycephalic bulldog to the long-limbed dolichocephalic saluki, found that genes greatly influence the behavior of the animal by their action on the conformation (and therefore locomotor or "manipulative" ability) of the body, but found little effect on the endocrine system.

Variations in agonistic behavior activity, emotionality and conditionability have been found (James, 1953). Some dogs, e.g., beagues can be housed in large numbers for they are non-aggressive; other more aggressive breeds are better kept in pairs or threes because the establishment of a hierarchical society involves much fighting which many continue if the social order is unstable. In mixed groups of dogs, it has been found that one particular breed is consistently dominant, so it is possible that dominance in genetically heterogeneous groups is determined by heredity (Pawlowski and Scott, 1956). Timidity may be influenced by environmental factors, i.e., the owner is dominant and the dog is a subordinate member of a group of animals, but inheritance of timidity has been suggested by Thorne (1944) who found that timid dogs were descendants of a very fearful bitch (Fig. 1).

We have a great variety of dogs who differ in many ways from their wolf ancestors and have developed behavior patterns not seen in the wolf (Scott, 1950). Inheritance of certain traits has a strong influence on later behavior, but it is the interaction of inherited (genetic) and environmental factors, especially early in life during the critical period of socialization, that dictates the behavior of the mature animal. Training to perform particular

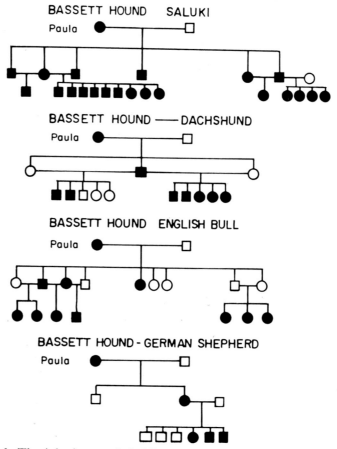

Figure 1. The inheritance of timidity. (The fear-biting hound was crossed with several breeds, shy dogs are represented in black symbols, friendly dogs in white.) (Redrawn from Thorne, 1944.)

tasks has been facilitated by selecting desirable traits which are inherited, and by adopting standard training procedures, the best results can be obtained. "Training" in this case is in effect the "environment" which interacts with the temperament or inherited constitution of the animal. It must be remembered that constitution may be altered by poor selective breeding, and consequently much compensatory training will be required. Also, traumatic experience due to environmental disturbances during the critical period of socialization, or lack of specific environmental stimulation (i.e., delayed socialization with man) may so alter the animal as to render it unsuitable for the particular activities that it was originally intended for by the dictates of its inherited temperament. Breed and strain differences are present among individual dogs, where environmental or inherited factors acting singly or together have a lesser or greater effect on the overt behavior of the animal.

Odor discrimination and tracking behavior have been studied by Whitney (1947) who finds some breeds are very adept at following trails but must be taught to discriminate different odors. By a backward learning procedure he teaches the dog to associate the odor with object or person and then the dog can be placed in a field and will follow the odor trail of a particular object presented to him. Buytendijk (1936) described some complicated studies of tracking behavior developed by European workers.

We must, however, be aware that training procedures for one type of dog may be ineffectual for another breed. Mild punishment is effective in inhibiting undesirable activities in beagles, for example, but punishing a terrier causes resistance, for these dogs are aggressive and pain is associated with fighting. Reward training is effective for most dogs, and food or handling are good reinforcing stimuli; the activity alone may be rewarding in itself, tracking dogs, for example, get considerable reinforcement by performing their chosen task. In complicated training procedures it is advisable to progress slowly, step by step, for overstimulation may cause confusion and inhibition of earlier learned responses; fixations or maladaptive responses may result and become habits which are difficult to eradicate. Forced training using a leash is popular among obedience schools; a command which acts as a conditioning stimulus followed by a tug on the leash is a simple conditioning procedure to train dogs to respond to command of voice. The leash can later be discarded once the conditioned response is established. Food reward may be used similarly. As motor coordination is well developed when the pup is approximately eight weeks of age, basic training including housebreaking, "come," "sit," and "fetch" can be undertaken. At a later age, when persistence and concentration are more stable, more complex tasks can be taught, commencing at about six months or a year of age, depending on the breed and degree of maturity. It must be remembered that training does not produce a new pattern of behavior, but rather it establishes control over the emergence of these patterns.

Social motivation (reward from the handler) is involved in the trainability of dogs. Pfaffenberger and Scott (1959) found that dogs who were not taken into homes before thirteen weeks of age from the breeding kennels were much less successful in training to become guide dogs for the blind, at twelve months of age. Socialization at the critical period therefore facilitates training irrespective of breed type and individual variability.

Breed differences in emotional behavior (Mahut, 1958) and shyness (Thorne, 1944) have been described. Avoidance training may cause unwanted timidity and, once established, avoidance behavior is difficult to extinguish (Solomon and Wynne, 1953); this is seen especially in shy and timid dogs socialized too late in life, i.e., after the optimum period between seven to twelve weeks of age. Restraint and restriction of activity with forced socialization and handling may eliminate these responses, although already indicated earlier, inherited factors may also be involved and act independently of environmental influences.

To summarize these several factors, the following points have been presented (Scott, 1954). Changes in behavior of domestic animals include increased genetic variability and modification of socialization with man (i.e., decreased wildness). Breed selection for the ability to learn specialized tasks has been carried further in the dog than in any other animal. The possession of dogs by semi-isolated human tribes in early times provided conditions for genetic change and each geographic region tended to have a different type of dog associated with that community. Experimental studies with five breeds of dogs and two hybrid crosses from this group were undertaken under standard environmental conditions (i.e., eliminating environmental variables) and motivational, social, emotional, physiological and learning tests were conducted at appropriate ages. A common genetic mechanism of inheritance was found in the inheritance of wildness, as determined by avoidance reactions in purebred and hybrid dogs. Generally, measures in differences in the threshold of stimulation in simple behavior patterns gave reasonably simple genetic results. Measures of complex adaptation did not give simple genetic results, possibly because adaptation consists of organization of the many capacities of the individual, which can take place in a variety of ways to produce the same effective result. Capacities which increased the ability to learn a special situation or task (i.e., adaptive behavior or learning) may limit the range of adaptability in other situations. This is important in selecting a breed for training to perform certain tasks.

Humphrey and Warner (1934) reported that defensive behavior is inherited, and also fear of noise (sound shyness) and touch (touch shyness) may be inherited independently, although early experience modifies the behavioral expression. Whitney (1947) notes that there are breed differences to pain sensitivity, terriers notably being very resistant. Krushinskii (1962) discusses the dominance of certain traits (or innate unconditioned reflexes) such as pointing, baying, setting, swimming, holding and carrying objects, and retrieving, and studied these traits in hybrid dogs. The selection of a behavior type greatly facilitates training to perform complicated activities based on the inherited behavioral characteristics. He notes that the passive defensive reflex (P.D.R.) i.e., shyness or cowardice, is inherited but manifest weakly if one parent has a weak P.D.R., although isolation during rearing greatly increases the P.D.R. The active defensive reflex (A.D.R.), i.e., aggression, is also an inherited unconditioned reflex, and is similarly influenced in early life, i.e., conditioned reflex or acquired "learned" behavior. Krushinskii studied the genotype and phenotype differences in these two important reflexes (the P.D.R. and A.D.R.). Airdales reared in partial isolation had greatly increased passive defensive reflexes than airdales reared as free ranging pets. Alsatians exhibited strong P.D.R. in both situations, and the reactions in the kenneled group were much stronger, indicating a breed difference. In both breeds, isolation reduced the A.D.R., while free range socialization increased the A.D.R. With doberman pinchers, a breed in which the P.D.R. is rarely seen, isolation only slightly increased this response. There are breed differences therefore in constitution (the innate components of behavior) and their susceptibility to environmental changes (acquired or conditioned responses). Socialization increases the A.D.R. and decreases the P.D.R., so that the animal can learn to overcome fears of new objects and becomes more aggressive and widely socialized. The initial reactions of a young dog to a novel situation or new, unaccustomed stimulus is a fear response (P.D.R.) and is followed by investigatory behavior (A.D.R.) which inhibits the earlier response. The work of Fuller (1962) who finds that there are breed differences in susceptibility to rearing in isolation during the critical period of socialization confirms these observations. Krushinskii suggests that wide socialization should be used to decrease the P.D.R. for disciplined working dogs, who should be selected from known stock having strong A.D.R. and weak P.D.R. It must be remembered that individual dogs show varying degrees of strength in these responses. Also these two activities may be combined in varying intensities in one animal; this is the aggressive-cowardly dog (frequently the fear-biting type) and are seen especially in litters from parent dogs of strong A.D.R. and P.D.R. respectively. Behavior of the aggressive-coward is an interaction of flight and fight reactions. To separate these reactions, Krushinskii gave morphine (0.08-0.04g) to different behavior types. He found that aggressive dogs were less aggressive (A.D.R. reduced) shy and fearful dogs showed little change, while aggressive-fearful dogs showed weakening of the A.D.R. and no change in the P.D.R. In this last group, there was dissociation of behavior, indicating that the behavior components are separable. (See Chapter 5 for further studies on breed differences in motor activity, excitability, A.D.R. and P.D.R.).

There are continuous transitions between innate and individually acquired behavior, so that instinctual and habitual processes are of evolutionary significance when one considers the adaptation of the species to the environment and the transmission of these acquired faculties to successive generations. Krushinskii (1962) expounds this concept and gives examples of such breeds that have an innate "desire" to retrieve, hunt, bay, and trail. Keeler and Trimble (1940) have described the innate drive in dalmatians to follow a carriage; the herding and droving behavior of sheep dogs appears early in life during play, and is stronger and more compulsive in those pups who will be excellent adult working dogs. The early emergence of such traits, e.g., herding in sheepdogs and pointing in gun dogs, facilitates the selection of desirable pups from the litter who strongly manifest these activities. Experience has shown that these dogs (who have an innate response which is reinforced by acquired training) are superior to their litter mates.

To quote Krushinskii (1962) ; "The unitary reactions and biological forms of behavior, in the formation of which innate unconditioned reflex components predominate, may be defined as instinctive behavioral acts. Unitary reactions and their more complex units—biological forms of behavior, in which individually acquired components predominate, are evidently behavioral acts which it is customary to call habits." With this concept, we may regard "instinct" as being made up of innate reflexes (e.g., feeding and locomotor reflexes, and active and passive defensive reflexes) which are inherited but which are modified by early experience; environmental stimuli alter these innate mechanisms, and the behavioral expression may differ. Behavior is therefore adaptive, and the act itself is in part therefore both innate and acquired. Krushinskii regards the unitary reactions of behavior as being composed of integrated unconditioned (innate, inherited) and conditioned (acquired) reflexes. Cowardice (strong passive defensive reflex) for example is inherited, but is also acquired as it is influenced by early experience, being manifest particularly by dogs reared in partial isolation.

Comparative Studies; Behavior and Socialization of Wolves

Attempts to tame wild adult timber wolves by different methods have revealed several intriguing results and give us a clearer meaning of phenomena such as flight distance; approach and avoidance behavior; fear biting; and extinction of fear responses by establishing positive psycho-social relationships. By comparing the social behavior patterns of their wild ancestors, the behavior of the dog and influences of selection and domestication may be more fully understood.

Freedman *et al.* (1961), working with dogs, found that if pups did not have contact with human beings until they were older than fourteen weeks of age (i.e., these pups were reared in complete isolation from humans) they were impossible to completely socialize and were literally wild and unapproachable. Social contact was made among other litters at selected ages and it was found that maximal socialization was obtained between six to eight weeks of age. During postnatal development, therefore, there is a period during which human contact is effective in establing a social bond, which is formed most strongly and permanently at six to eight weeks of age. Before and after this period socialization is less stable, and at fourteen weeks is impossible to establish. This phenomenon resembles "imprinting" (Hess, 1958) in other animals and ensures that the animal is socialized early in life with its own species. Socialization with other species may occur during this sensitive period between six to eight weeks and is the best time for domesticating puppies in the household environment. After this sensitive period when approach behavior is strong (i.e., "friendliness") inhibition occurs with the development of avoidance behavior (i.e., fearfulness) which under natural conditions would keep the pup with its litter mates to whom it has already been socialized and at a safe distance from strange animals who may possibly be predators. Russian work employing Pavlovian conditioning techniques supports these behavior studies in that the dog develops through a period critical to the formation of primary social relationships, where approach and later avoidance behavior patterns operate (Mirzakamirova *et al.*, 1958).

With this knowledge of the importance of early experience modifying social behavior in later life, Ginsburg undertook the task of attempting to socialize wild adult timber wolves. These animals were trapped in their natural habitats in North America and were kept in excellent health throughout the experimental period. Social studies were also done on two groups of captive wolves, and a brief review of these observations will be given first.

Several behavior patterns of the wolf are present in the dog, while the effects of domestication and selective breeding on this latter species, have, however, reduced other behavior patterns such as pack-group co-ordinated (allelomimetic) activities and social hierarchy relationships. In the pack, activities are controlled by a single dominant male wolf.

Submissive postures, including slinking with the ears laid back and tail tucked between legs and lying on the back were observed. Bowing of the neck to a more dominant adversary was not seen in these groups. Comparative studies of wolves, coyotes, dingoes and dogs have revealed that the domestic dog appears to be a wolf with no behavioral capacities added, but with many behavior patterns modified or reduced. Almost all of the behavior seen in dogs is also seen in wolves, but in addition has fuller significance in wolves (Ginsburg and Slatis, 1962). While vocalization and postural attitudes in coyotes, dingoes and wolves have consistent meaning, threat behavior of the dog was less predictable, so that a trained observer in the experimental studies was able to interact more safely with a wild Canid. A challenge from the latter is unmistakable, while a challenge from a domesticated dog has little predictive value unless the individual dog is well known.

Of these groups of wild Canidae, wolves are the most gregarious in nature and were easiest to tame and are gregarious toward humans. Coyotes and dingoes are less gregarious and tend to be one-mannish under confinement. Most Canids wean their offspring, while the wolf continues to feed regurgitated food to the young until they are six to eight months old. The effects of tranquillization using librium also differed between coyotes and wolves. In wolves, there is no effect on wolf with wolf interactions, but with a handler the wolf is less fearful and more likely to challenge and snap at the experimenter. In coyotes, tranquilization reduced the threats and dominant gestures of a dominant animal, thus changing the social relationship within the coyote group, and also permits easy approach by the experimenter who is not threatened in the usual manner (Ginsberg and Slatis, 1962).

A group of coyotes and wolves born in captivity and reared under varying schedules of socialization to humans have been studied (Ginsberg et al., 1962.) All animals showed residual wildness in the form of low thresholds and extreme reactions (fear and shyness) to novel situations. Threat and attack were more common when the animals were in close confinement in small cages, and withdrawal occurred when there was space to avoid the investigator. Effects of socialization were largely extinguished if not reinforced at frequent intervals as the subjects matured. Fully socialized wolves were gregarious to humans.

Socialization with wild adult animals was achieved after long passive-active human-wolf interactions respectively. Eventually approach investigatory behavior was seen; the wolf moved slowly and hesitantly toward the experimenter. Fear responses were at this time at a critical point, for during approach the flight distance was being reduced by the exploratory drive of the subject. As wolves are primarily gregarious animals, this eventual extinction of fear responses in a social situation is facilitated. During this critical period, the reactions of the experimenter were crucial. Any sudden movement by him would cause unpredictable responses in the wolf, for the ambivalency of response was maximal at this time.

Once the wolf approached the passive human, approach behavior increased on subsequent trials until eventually bodily contact was made. Physical bodily contact and non-aggressive approach behavior marked the establishment of a psycho-social relationship between man and wolf which was reinforced by daily social interactions and contact between subject and experimenter. The ambivalency of behavior seen earlier disappeared, and responsiveness could be predicted in the behavior patterns of the wolf prior to and during the experiment, which expressed precisely how the subject would react.

Inherited Abnormalities

Burns (1952) has given a comprehensive review of the genetics of the dog and discusses the inheritance of reproductive capacities, conformation, coat color, behavioral attributes and physiological peculiarities, abnormalities and disease. These latter points we must consider in greater detail.

Recessive factors may be inherited and emerge when inbreeding is practiced or when a dog favored by breeders for special characteristics is bred with a large number of dogs. The emergence of these recessive traits may be undesirable, e.g., cleft palate in the bulldog, but, as these factors are linked to a particular strain, they arise frequently and are difficult to eliminate. It is the responsibility of the dog breeder to recognize these undesirable factors and to eliminate them by not using affected animals, or animals transmitting the undesirable traits. A wide variety of these abnormalities at the behavioral and morphological levels have been recorded among different breeds, and these develop independently of environmental influences or are such that an unfavorable environment combined with an inherited diathesis (or susceptibility) may cause precipitation of the undesirable trait. Deterioration of the breed type occurs as inbreeding causes the emergence of recessive factors. Several dogs in America have gone this way, the English setter, for example; some specimens resemble frail long-legged spaniels.

At the behavioral level we see great temperamental differences immediately between show dogs and the working counterparts of the same breed. The German shepherd, for example, is an excellent working dog, but the show specimen may be unpredictable, aggressive or extremely shy and difficult to socialize. As a certain breed becomes popular, breeders produce more dogs to satisfy public demands, and this has happened especially in the toy poodle and cocker spaniel. There are several reports of a particular strain being either very timid, hyperactive, aggressive or fear biting.

Intensive breeding has resulted in numerous congenital anomalies at the morphological level (Hodgman, 1962). Hip dysplasia in German shepherds and retrievers (especially in show strains that have been bred to look "racey" and low and tapering at the hips) ; retinal degeneration in the poodle and setter; lens luxation in the fox terrier; luxated patellae in toy breeds, especially the poodle, where rotation of the tibial crest and shallowness of the trochlea of the femur causes medial luxation of the patella; deafness in white bull terriers and Dalamatians; idiopathic epilepsy in poodles, and cocker spaniels; cryptorchidism, entropion, intereretebral disc luxation, and esophageal dilation and hemophilia in several breeds. Also some breeds may be more susceptible to disease than others (Parry, 1950; Fox *et al.,* 1964) .

Breeding for certain physical characteristics may cause disease because of the direct influence of these characteristics which would, in nature, prejudice the survival of the animal. Heavy long breeds of dog, e.g., Welsh corgi and dachshund, are very prone to intervertebral disk luxation. Breeding for woolly coat features has been associated with severe ear trouble in poodles and Bedlington terriers; the external auditory meatus develops an excessive growth of hair. One of the most grotesque examples of selective breeding is seen in the brachycephalic (blunt faced) dogs, such as the pekingese and the bulldog. Excessive folds of skin (due perhaps to selective reduction of the skeleton) give rise to dermatitis in the skin folds, and excess of soft tissues, i.e., soft palate, and deformity of the alae of the nostrils may be so severe that the larynx or treachea collapses and the animal suffocates, or the deformities are such that its whole life is spent under restricted activity due to partial suffocation (Leonard, 1960, Fox 1963.)

References

Burns, M.: *The Genetics of the Dog*. Tech Comm. No. 9, Commonwealth Bureau Animal Breeding and Genetics, Farmham Bucks, England, Comm. Agric. Bureaux, 1952.

Buytendijk, F. J. J.: *The Mind of the Dog*. Boston, Houghton-Mifflin, 1936.

Fox, M. W.: Developmental abnormalities of the canine skull. *Canad. J. Comp. Med. and Vet. Sci., 27*:9:219-222, 1963.

Fox, M. W., Hoag, W. G. and Stroud, J.: Breed susceptibility and etiology of endemic colioform enteritis in the dog. *Lab. animal care*, (1964) in press.

Freedman, D. G., Elliott, E. and King, J. A.: Critical period in the social development of dogs. *Science, 133*:1016-1017, 1961.

Fuller, J. L. and Thompson, W. R.: *Behavior Genetics*. New York, Wiley, 1960.

Fuller, J. L. and Scott, J. P.: Heredity and learning in infrahuman mammals. *Eugen. Quart., 1*:28-43, 1954.

Fuller, J. L.: Programmed life histories, and socialization of the dog. *Trans. 3rd Int. Congress Psychiat.*, Montreal, 1961.

Fuller, J. L.: Hereditary differences in trainability of purebred dogs. *J. Genet. Psychol., 87*:229-238, 1955.

Ginsburg, B. E. and Slatis, H.: The use of purebred dogs in research. Problems of Genetics, *Proc. Animal Care Panel, 12*:4:151-156, 1962.

Ginsburg, B. E., Woolpy, J., Kleiman, D. and Edwards, C.: Comparative studies of canine behavior. III. Socialization to humans on varying schedules of experience and of tranquillizing drugs. *Amer. Zoöl., 2*:3:144, 1962.

Hess, E. S.: Imprinting in animals. *Sci. Amer., 193*:3:81-90, 1958.

Hodgman, S. F. J.: Abnormalities of possible hereditary origin in dogs. *Vet. Rec., 74*:46:1239-1246, 1962.

Humphrey, E. and Warner, L.: *Working Dogs*. Baltimore, Williams & Wilkins Co., 1934.

James, W. T.: Social organization among dogs of different temperaments; terriers and beagles, reared together. *J. Comp. Physiol. Psychol., 44*:71-77, 1951.

James, W. T.: Morphological and constitutional factors in conditioning. *An. N. Y. Acad. Sci., 56*:2, 117-183, 1953.

Keeler, C. E. and Trimble, H. C.: Inheritance of position preference in coach dogs. *J. Hered., 31*:2:51-54, 1940.

Krushinskii, L. V.: *Animal Behavior*. New York, Consultant Bureau, 1962.

Leonard, H. C.: Collapse of larynx and adjacent structures in the dog. *J. Am. Vet. M. A., 137*:6:360-363, 1960.

Mahut, H.: Breed differences in the dog's emotional behaviour. *Canad. J. Psychol., 12*:35-44, 1958.

Mirzakarimova, M. G., Stel'mkh, L. N. and Troshikhin, V. A.: Directed changes in passive-defensive and investigatory reflexes in ontogenesis. *Pavlov J. Higher Nerv. Activity, 8*:5, 1958.

Pawlowski, A. A. and Scott, J. P.: Hereditary differences in the development of dominance in a litter of puppies. *J. Comp. Physiol. Psychol., 49*:353-358, 1956.

Pfaffenberger, C. J.: *Training Your Spaniel*. New York, Putnam, 1947.

Pfaffenberger, C. J. and Scott, J. P.: The relationship between delayed socialization and trainability in guide dogs. *J. Genet. Psychol., 95*:145-155, 1959.

Pfaffenberger, C. J.: *The New Knowledge of Dog Behavior*. New York, Howell Book House, Inc., 1963.

Saunders, B.: *Training You to Train Your Dog*. New York, Doubleday, 1952.

Scott, J. P.: The effects of selection and domestication upon the behavior of the dog. *J. Nat. Cancer Inst., 15*:739-758, 1954.

Scott, J. P.: The social behavior of dogs and wolves; an illustration of sociobiological systems. *Am. New York Acad. Sci., 51*:6:1009-1021, 1950.

Solomon, R. L. and Wynne, L. C.: Traumatic avoidance learning: acquisition in normal dogs. *Psychol. Monogr., 67*:4:1-19, 1953.

Stockard, C. R., Anderson, O. D. and James, W. T.: *Genetic and Endocrine Basis for Differences in Form and Behavior*. Philadelphia, Wistar Inst. Press, 1941.

Thorne, F. C.: The inheritance of shyness in dogs. *J. Genet Psychol., 65*:275-279, 1944.

Whitney, L. F.: *How to Breed Dogs*. New York, Orange Judd, 1947.

Whitney, L. F.: Inheritance of mental aptitudes in dogs. *Proc. 6th Internat. Congress Genetics, 2*:211-212, 1932.

Chapter 5

EXPERIMENTAL PSYCHOBIOLOGY

M ANY PROBLEMS of human behavior where social, environmental and genetic factors are involved and which affect and modify normal psychological or physiological development have been studied theoretically in the dog by experimental manipulation and control of these factors. The effects of maternal deprivation, separation, emotional experience and psychological trauma in early life have been investigated, notably by Scott and Fuller. The safety and effectiveness of psychopharmacological drugs are assayed on the behavioral level. Normal development and the development of affectional behavior and learning have been studied, and, by the use of inbred strains, genetic influences may be investigated. By control of environmental and social experience, further elements contributory to adult behavior may be discovered.

Critical periods in the process of socialization and other effects on early experience. The development of the neonate dog involves both motor and sensory maturation. Sudden modifications and changes of behavior are seen at about three weeks of age and this time is regarded as the onset of the critical period of socialization. The theory of the critical periods plays a major role in research on the effects of early experience on later behavior (Scott and Marston, 1950; Scott and Fuller, 1954; Scott, 1958 & 1962). This has been explored experimentally. If social contact is permitted at this time for only a short period, the infant animal is facilitated in the formation of social relationships. Normally this relationship is made with a member of the same species, but, in the domestic dog, relationships with human beings are made at an early age within this critical period. Experience at this time therefore determines the close relationships and affects later social behavior in adult life. The principal positive mechanisms involved in the dog are approach, play and investigative responses: fear and escape responses are the main negative mechanisms. The escape response does not develop if the puppy is reared in complete isolation during the critical period (Waller and Fuller, 1961). These animals lose the capacity to make positive contacts with humans but have not lost the emotional capacities to respond to them. The effects of unfamiliarity of environment, social competition or facilitation and allelomimetic (group coordinated) behavior have also been studied in earlier work in young dogs (Scott *et al.*, 1950).

The effects of extensive social contacts with humans at different ages have been observed and results confirm the critical period hypothesis in that the maximum effects on socialization are obtained between five to seven weeks of age (Freedman, 1958; Freedman *et al.*, 1961). It is now possible to roughly locate similar periods of development in dogs and human infants (Scott, 1963). Both are highly protected from environmental effects before the onset of the critical period, but difference is seen in the human where the period of primary socialization precedes the major transition to adult behavior patterns.

The effect of social isolation on emotional behavior, using yelping activity as an indicator of emotional behavior, has been found to be most marked between five to seven weeks of age (Scott and Elliot, 1961). Using yelping as a similar emotional indicator, restraint, and combination of isolation and restraint have also been explored (Ross *et al.*, 1960). Sound spectrograph analysis of distress vocalization is a useful tool employed as an objective measurement of emotional expression (Scott, 1960). Overnight isolation of puppies between the ages of five to seven weeks (as would happen in the home) causes emotional disturbances as evaluated by distress vocalization. The immediate result is to speed the processes of socialization and the animal develops a more rapid attachment to its human handler. When these animals are restored to their normal environment and given normal experiences with handlers, the earlier effects of the emotional experience quickly disappear, indicating that the infant animal has a good capacity for spontaneous recovery under normal environmental conditions.

Dogs have been reared completely separated from human beings until they are taken into the laboratory for the first time at different ages for primary socialization with man. Social contact has little effect until four weeks of age. A peak capacity to form positive emotional attachment is reached between five to seven weeks of age, and after this there is a decline in the ability to form social relationships. Dogs separated until fourteen weeks of age are literally wild and unapproachable, and almost impossible to socialize (Freedman *et al.*, 1961). Social contact with dogs reared singly in solitary isolation, even for a brief period of time within the critical period, is effective in establishing social relationships between man and dog. The relationship between delayed socialization and trainability has been noted (Scott and Pfaffenberger, 1959), and the effects of differential human handling as reinforcing events and as treatment influencing later social behavior have also been studied (Stanley 1958; Stanley and Elliot, 1962).

Sucking behavior and the effects of early experience modifying later ingestive behavior in the young dog have been investigated (Ross *et al.*, 1957; Scott *et al.*, 1959). Several observations are comparable to the effects of early experience on sucking behavior in human infants, where learning by conditioning and reflexive behavior interact and are modified by certain factors influencing ingestive behavior (Elliot and King, 1959).

Psychopharmacological drugs have been used to analyze the physiological nature of emotions by using tranquilizing or stimulant drugs (e.g., Chlorpromazine or Amphetamine). Extensive motivation and emotionality as a result of isolation and fear of a strange environment have been modified by these drugs. Results indicate the favorable effects in some cases where chemotherapy may be applied in the treatment of behavioral disorders where emotional (physiological and psychological) effects can be reduced (Fuller *et al.*, 1950; Fuller, 1962).

These drugs have also been used to determine their effects on perceptual and social learning in the developing animal. In the adult animal these drugs modify well established behavior patterns, depressing or stimulating some and leaving others near normal. As yet no developmental behavioral abnormalities or retardation of normal development have been recorded in tranquilized semi-isolated puppies. (Semi-isolation means that animals were housed singly with no social contacts other than scheduled daily contact with the observer.) Capacity for adaptive behavior is unimpaired.

Large doses of Chlorpromazine in the adult dog disrupt trained discrimination procedures (lifting a bar with nose to obtain food) and performance is poor in trained animals. Low doses of this drug however increase the rates of response.

Developmental studies of learning were investigated to ascertain when the newborn animal first begins to learn and to interact with its environment. It is possible to condition puppies prior to three weeks of age but there is instability of the conditioning response indicating that learning processes have not yet fully developed (Fuller, *et al*, 1950; Fuller and Cornwell, 1959). More stable responses are seen in older puppies, from eighteen to twenty days of age onwards. Central stimulatory drugs speed the conditioning processes while tranquilizers prevented the appearance of the conditioned responses. There is no interference of learning with these drugs.

Genetic Studies. Data have been collected from long term studies of the effects of heredity on the strain and individual differences in behavior and trainability (Scott and Charles, 1954; Fuller, 1956; Scott and Fuller, 1964). Using five inbred strains of dogs, identical training was given to each individual, and it was found that there was no average increase or decrease in the bahavioral expression of the genetic differences between these animals. In general these behavior traits show considerable overlap between breeds, and, as no breed is genetically uniform, a great deal of individual variation is allowed. The seasonal breeding cycle and relative barklessness of the African basenji have been studied. Both these traits showed an unusual inheritance pattern in that the F_1 generation was intermediate and as variable as the F_2's. Estrus tended to be irregular in these hybrids, some showing a stronger tendency to the seasonal monestrus of one parent or a stronger tendency towards the diestrus cycles of the other parent, or a highly variable combination of both cycles. Cocker spaniels were used in these cross breeding studies. These results indicate how simple Mendelian mechanisms may be complicated by physiological interactions (Scott and Fuller, 1959; Scott *et al.,* 1960).

The effects of heredity on social behavior have been investigated by raising puppies of different breeds and hybrids in a uniform environment. Each animal is given a variety of behavioral tests. Individual sexual, genetic, aggressiveness and social dominance factors are involved. A greater proportion of dominant animals was found in the segregated hybrids than in nonsegregated hybrids and pure breeds. These results suggest a general concept "that the differentiation of social relationships is proportional to the magnitude of the differences in basic physiological and psychological capacities of the individuals" (Fuller, 1956). A general survey has revealed that the hereditary capacities of a breed are formed from a large number of special traits combined with a few general ones.

Social Isolation Studies (Fuller, 1964). These developed from studies of drug effects in puppies reared in semi-isolation. It has been found that puppies in complete isolation from three weeks of age, but given seventy-five minutes social contact with man in toto, develop normally. Those isolated and not given this social contact between four to fifteen weeks of age show behavior deficits from which recovery is slow. Further experimentation may define with greater precision the minimal experience-time requirement for neutralizing the effects of isolation.

Dogs restricted of social experience between the ages of four to sixteen weeks develop an "isolation syndrome," characterized by extereme activity reduction in the intensity of social contacts and decreased manipulative behavior. Abnormal behavior was also obtained by punishing animals on a systematic schedule over the same period of the life span. These latter animals are reared therefore under semi-isolation. Reduced activity and avoidance of responses which had been followed by punishment are characteristic of the punishment syndrome (Fuller, personal communication), although punished animals soon recovered once the inhibitory stimuli were discontinued and approached the experimenter. It was found that dogs reared in isolation are greatly handicapped in a competitive social situation, where avoidance behavior of man and other dogs dominates approach responses (Fisher, 1955).

Chlorpromazine is used as a tranquilizer to reduce the trauma of the psychological experience and to modify recovery. Recovery from the punishment syndrome is not influenced by the drug, but recovery from the isolation syndrome is enhanced. These results are of psychiatric interest because the isolation syndrome dogs show some symptoms similar to those of so-called autistic children.

More recent work on the amelioration of the isolation syndrome has shown that allowing the animal to leave its isolation quarters spontaneously instead of forcing contacts, and tranquilization with chlorpromazine are helpful in reducing fear responses. Wirehaired terriers are less affected than beagles, indicating a breed difference. These data indicate that the events surrounding the emergence from the isolation are critical to the origin and persistence of the syndrome as a mass fear response. The slow recovery from the syndrome does not indicate the time lag in the learning of new responses, but rather the gradual removal of a rigid activity pattern. Some subjects showed complete social and manipulative recovery almost immediately after emergence (Fuller, 1964). Isolation after the critical period of socialization produces less severe behavior changes in older dogs (Angermeier and James, 1961; Thompson and Heron, 1954).

Developmental studies of affectional behavior have been designed in relation to socialization where hereditary and experiential factors controlling positive social responses and affectional behavior towards people can be investigated. Differential handling and the effects of this are evaluated in the reactions of puppies towards the handler on later occasions. Breed differences and the effects of early experience are also included in these studies. The major finding in this field so far is that mere contact with a passive handler is remarkably strong in maintaining approach behavior of the puppy. This and correlated findings have important implications for such clinico-psychological concepts as affection hunger and overdependency in man (Stanley, 1958; Stanley and Elliot, 1962).

It was found that puppies ran faster and showed a stronger positive response towards a passive observer than to one who had previously petted the animal. These findings are consistent in aggressive breeds (basenji and basenji-fox terrier hybrids) and may indicate that petting is a form of dominance over the puppy and that reward is greater in social contact with a passive observer. These dogs ran faster towards a passive observer than to a handling person. Shetland sheepdogs however ran equally as fast to both active and passive persons. "Operant" conditioning techniques were used in these experiments, the T maze apparatus being a useful tool for statistical evaluation of observational data (Fig. 1) from studies of learning in sub-primates.

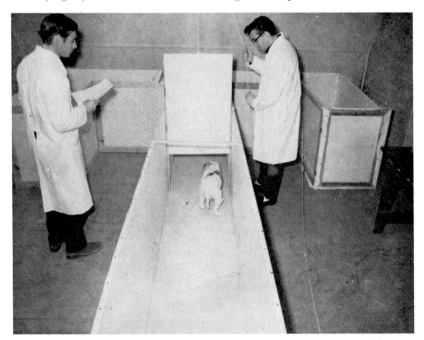

Figure 1. The T maze apparatus, used to evaluate learning ability & breed differences in motivation.

Experiments designed to influence the behavior of young dogs by reward or punishment (e.g., Fisher's approach punishment schedule of pups reared in isolation (1955) and food deprivation used by Elliot and King (1960), have given results indicating that the processes of forming a social attachment is independent of these influences of reward or punishment. During the critical period of socialization the pup will become attached to any animal that it comes into contact with for a certain time, irrespective of the type of emotional experience with it. Intense emotional experience, whether rewarding or punishing, increases the speed of forming the primary social relationship.

Russian Studies

Recent work on the typological features of the nervous system, using Pavlov's interpretations (Ivamov-Smolenski, 1954), includes an interesting report on the rhythmical patellar reflex in relation to the different types of nervous system of the dog, which serves as a good illustration of the Pavlovian concepts (Borbrova, 1961).

Type of Nervous System	Strength		Balance		Predominance		Susceptible of Breakdown	Type of Breakdown
	Strong	Weak	Bal.	Unbal.	Excitation	Inhibition		
Sanguine	+		+				—	
Phlegmatic	+		+				—	
Choleric	+			+	+		+	excitatory
Melancholic		+		+		+	+	inhibitory

(Table adapted from Babkin, 1938.)

The stability of response of the patellar reflex was found to be proportional to the balance of the nervous system, i.e., equality of inhibitory and excitatory processes. The amplitude of response was dependent more on the strength of the excitatory process than on the degree of predominance of the excitatory over inhibitory process. This was greatest in dogs of the "strong" type of nervous system. Susceptibility to inhibition was found to increase with the strength of the dog's type of nervous system. With a very inert nervous system, there was a decline of liability to inhibit the reflex as the rate of reflex contractions increased, but there was more ready inhibition as rate increased with dogs having a better nervous process mobility. Such variations are thought to be the cortical components of the reflex arc. Different responses of autonomic and spinal reflexes may be accounted for on the Pavlovian theory that animals with different cortical components of the nervous processes manifest variable conditioned responses at all levels of the nervous system.

Further experimentation on the basis of Pavlovian conditioning has been reported (James, 1934) where correlations were made between morphological form and behavior type; hysterical and inhibitable types of dog were described. The genetic and endocrine basis for differences in form and behavior have been studied in a monumental work by Stockard *et al.* (1941). Selective breeding produced strains which have behavioral differences which may be related to both morphology and the endocrine system, e.g., some breeds normally have hyperactive thyroids and are behaviorally more active (see Chapter 4).

The development of external inhibition of conditioned reflexes reported by Stel'makh (1950) using a rattle noise to inhibit the conditioned motor-alimentary conditioned reflex established at seventeen days of age, presents some interesting results. At twenty to twenty-three days of age, no external inhibition of the conditioned reflex occurred on application of the extra inhibitory stimulus, and it was thought that it was because at this age investigatory behavior is at its peak and conditioned reflexes are most readily formed. Marked inhibition of the conditioned reflex occurred from twenty-four to forty days; the pups refused to eat and often neurotic behavior was seen. From forty to forty-five days the intensity of external inhibition diminished. At two to three months of age external inhibition was absent and extra stimuli caused generalization of the conditioned reflex. In some pups very weak inhibition was seen and also passive defensive reactions. At four months of age external inhibition increased and was more so at six months of age at which time extra stimuli caused neurotic behavior. With increasing physical strength of the inhibitory agent, external inhibition increased at all ages except during the two to three month period. Adjustment by training was seen in some pups. Individual variability may have been due to inherited factors. It was also observed that during the periods in which passive defensive reactions were seen external inhibition was strong while in periods where passive defensive reactions were absent and investigatory reflexes predominant inhibition was slight or absent. Between twenty to thirty days and two to three months external inhibition was almost completely absent. Generalized inhibition of the conditioned reflex at twenty to twenty-five days was thought to be due to insufficient maturity of the cerebral cortex coupled with a high excitable threshold.

As inhibition increased at twenty to forty days, passive defensive reactions occurred. These data support in part Western observations on trainability and learning, where similar "classical" and "operant" conditioning techniques are used. Training to perform particular tasks will be discussed in Chapter 9 in the light of these experimental results. In another study, changes in passive defensive and investigatory reflexes appear between thirty to forty-five days and are strong up to six months. Passive defensive reactions were weak at two to two and-a-half months but strong from three to four months onward. In animals of the same age, if investigatory reflexes were strong, then passive defensive responses were weak, and vice versa. Training and heredity influence the passive defensive reaction. It was concluded that conditioning of the unconditional reflex was most effective when the unconditioned response first appeared; training is therefore most effective at this time, when it is easily reinforced and intensified (Mirzakamirova *et al.*), 1958).

Krushinskii (1962) reports that drug induced hyperthyroidism increases the excitability of conditioned reflexes and increases both active (ADR) and passive defensive reactions (PDR), while surgically induced hypothyroidism decreases excitability and decreases PDR and ADR. Castration of the male dog weakens cortical activity, according to Russian workers, and decreases the processes of stimulation and inhibition. Ovariectomy has little or no effect, but the female is less cowardly (reduced PDR) during estrus. Anderson (1941) reports similar results. According to Krushinskii, the nervous system of the female is weaker than that of the male, for female dogs are more difficult to train complicated tasks under difficult conditions (because the PDR is stronger than in the male) while the male is more able to form individually acquired skills under frustrating and difficult conditions and is more resistant to loud noises (i.e., ADR stronger in the male dog). Using sex hormones, he found that androgens in-

creased ADR while estrogens had some slight effect on PDR. Sex
differences are insignificant, because they reflect only indirectly
the differences in the degree of the strength of the nervous system
in the male and female (Krushinskii, 1962).

The following account of Russian concepts (Krushinskii,
1962) is presented, and it is interesting that results have been obtained by these workers that are very similar to observations
in western countries where different concepts and techniques
were applied. Behavioral activity is an index of excitability, and
strength and excitability of the nervous system facilitate trainability (or the establishment of condtioned reflexes). Caffeine
increases excitability up to an optimum and then causes inhibition. Success in the formation of an individually acquired habit
is proportional to the degree of excitability. Stimulants (caffeine
and thyroidin) increase excitability and therefore improve performance. Very active dogs are not the best subjects for scent
trailing and are harder to train as some control and inhibition is
required. The general level of excitability is important in the
manifestation and expression of unitary reactions of behavior.
Wolves and huskies have little motor excitability (i.e., are unexcitable) and have a strong PDR, which is weakly manifest
because of the low degree of motor excitation. Hybrid dogs of
these two groups are very fearful and active, for the strong PDR
of one parent (wolf or husky) is combined with the great motor
excitability of the other parent (dog). Some difficulties are encountered in determining the behavior type, for some dogs show
extreme PDR in a strange environment and will not react to
stimuli, while in a familiar environment they show a high degree
of excitability. Generally a high degree of excitability is associated
with a strong PDR.

Cocaine (2.5 mgm/Kg) given to unexcitable dogs with weak
PDR caused increased strength of the PDR (i.e., dogs were more
cowardly) and were more excitable (a pedometer recorded this
as an activity index). In these unexcitable dogs, cocaine therefore
increased excitability which reduced the (genotype or innate)
threshold of the PDR, for cocaine increases the excitability of dogs
that have no PDR. The degree of excitability therefore influences
the expression of the PDR. Cocaine also increases ADR and ex-

citation. Aggressive-cowardly dogs given cocaine reacted variably, some were more aggressive or more cowardly (i.e., dissociation occurred) while others were only more active and showed no dissociation. This effect therefore depends on the original strength and balance between the ADR and PDR. A strong ADR may completely inhibit a weaker PDR as excitation, which increases both these reflexes, increases the negative balance between them.

Cowardly dogs do not have a weak nervous system, as was thought by earlier Pavlovian workers, although frequently a strong PDR is associated with a weak nervous system (e.g., the dog cannot bear loud noises). Inheritance and early experience are doubly interacting factors here. With a strong nervous system, the PDR is often absent. Isolation of dogs with a strong nervous system during early life has a lesser effect, for the strong ADR facilitates inhibition of the PDR or fearful responses. A strong nervous system can inhibit the PDR while a weak nervous system cannot. The ADR depends on early experience which inhibits the initial PDR to new stimuli during socialization, therefore, dogs with a strong ADR learn better and are easier to socialize because they are innately less fearful. Rearing "free range" (in large enclosures) increases the ADR which therefore outbalances and inhibits the PDR. Krushinskii, in relation to the work of Stockard, James and Anderson (1941) on the endocrine and morphologic differences in behavior, describes two main canine types. One is athletic and wide bodied; this type has great strength of the nervous system with low excitability. The other is the slender narrow-bodied type, which has increased excitability and a weaker nervous system.

Effect of Brain Lesions on Behavior

Little information is available on experimental studies of the effect of brain lesions on behavior. Dukes (1955) has reviewed the work of Goltz, who studied the effects of decortication (removal of the cerebral hemispheres) in the dog. Corpora striati thalami and corpora quadrigemina were also injured. The subject lived for eighteen months; fairly good locomotion was possible. The animal showed hunger, could eat, and digestion was good although the condition of the subject was only moderate;

a weak startle reflex to sound was present; vision was severely affected for objects were run into, although a strong light flash caused the animal to blink and turn its head away. Olfaction was abolished although the sense of taste was thought not to be impaired. The sense of touch was also impaired but painful stimuli evoked avoidance behavior, snapping and barking. Psychic functions (fear, affection, pleasure and sexual interest) were absent. Persons and other dogs were not recognized, and hearing ability and memory were gone. More recent work has shown that if the corpus striatum, interbrain and midbrain are spared, psychic disturbances are less profound and some learning ability is retained. Wilker (1951) has also reported the long-term effects of removal of the neocortex in the dog. Some years ago when leucotomy (prefontal lobectomy) was first performed on human patients to alleviate intractable psychoneuroses, several experiments were performed on mammals to see how such a surgical procedure would affect behavior. Prefrontal lobectomy in the dog apparently reduces anxiety (Speakman and Babkin 1950), as in man, and in conditioning experiments where dogs were inhibited from feeding, deprivation caused less anxiety in operated dogs than in control subjects (Lichtenstein, 1950). Feeding-inhibition responses were developed pre-operatively in these dogs, and, after leucotomy, maladaptive responses were studied. Some loss of feeding inhibition was noted, and feeding inhibition could be reestablished slightly less easily than before. There was therefore a deficit in the formation and retention of conditioned responses, and it was thought that fear responses and anxiety were extinguished as a result of the surgical lesion. With a decreased capacity to form conditioned fear responses, these dogs could be tamed more easily, but the social position would never be balanced as fear for superiors is lost. Lawicka (1957) has studied the effects of prefrontal lobectomy on vocal conditioned reflexes. The effect of temporal lobe lesions on the dog has been explored (Fuller et al., 1957). It was found that dogs were less responsive to stimuli in general, but not incapable of responding appropriately to the stimuli when they were persistent enough to elicit a response. No changes in affective behavior were observed. With a handler, these dogs were less timid post operatively, but in a competitive feeding situation with control dogs, they were no longer dominant and were non-competitive. No marked alterations in sexual behavior were observed, but gross impairment of discrimination-type tests was seen, indicating that the surgical lesion may have interfered with a focus for visually guided behavior. Different breeds were used in this study and it was suggested that as the rearing and early experience conditions were the same for all these animals, an inherited or early acquired neural organization may be as effective as brain damage in determining the effective behavior of a particular member of a species.

The electroencephalogram gives useful data on the activity of the brain, and has wide application to behavior studies. More recent techniques including permanently implanted electrodes and transistorized telemetric recording devices will give results of greater significance, for more specific areas of the brain may be studied (Himwich and Hambrecht 1963). With telemetry, the animal may be studied some distance from the observer who may be several rooms away. Variables such as the presence of the experimenter, which may establish certain conditioned responses, or entry of a stranger into the experimental room causing sudden autonomic changes in the subject (e.g., elevated temperature and increased heart rate) are eliminated. The characteristics of surface and internal temperatures of dogs presented with conditioned and unconditioned stimuli have been studied (Chambers and Fuller, 1958). The temperature responses of the pinna, muzzle, and rectum were recorded, the muzzle being the most sensitive area. Abrupt decline in temperature was seen in association with conditioned responses, and may be due to autonomic vasoconstriction of the blood vessels. The results suggest that temperature responses during various experimental treatments are useful indicators of autonomic arousal. Recently, techniques have been developed to study the effects of certain drugs on behavior (Himwich et al., 1960) by injection into selected arterial sites of the brain. By surgical procedures involving vascular anastomosis of carotid and vertebral arteries, and occlusion of vascular components of the circle of Willis, psychopharmacological agents can be administered intra-arterially to produce an effect on selected areas of the brain supplied by the surgically altered arterial circulation. The different effects of the same drug when given intravenously or intra-arterially can be compared. Biochemical analysis of the brain can be made after treatment, to detect specific sites of drug action on the brain in relation to the route of injection, and correlate such findings with the behavior of the animal observed during the experiment.

Intra-cerebral injection of drugs into the unrestrained animal, via a cannula implanted in a lateral ventricle, has been performed in several studies to evaluate behavioral effects of certain drugs. Haley and McCormick (1956) reported the effects of intra-cerebral injection of lysergic acid, (L.S.D.) : they observed regression of behavior to puppy-like activities, similar to symptoms seen occasionally in man. They concluded that this technique is useful in the investigation of certain psychopharmacologic drugs, and has the notable advantages that the animal is unre strained so that the behavioral expression of direct drug action on the brain can be observed.

The effect of a certain drug or brain lesion on the ability of the dog to perform a particular task has been studied by establishing a simple conditioned response prior to treatment. By this means the pre and post-treatment responses, (conditioned pain avoidance, sound discrimination and food reward for example) can be compared, and the effect of treatment evaluated. Nemenov (1934) used the conditioned reflex method to investigate the effect of roentgen rays on the brain; Tunturi (1955) studied the effects of lesions of the auditory cortex on conditioned reflexes, and Allen, reported several studies on the effects of the tactile cortex, pyramidal tracts, motor and olfactory areas on conditioned tactile, olfactory and motor conditioned responses (1946) . The conditioned response technique is a useful means of assessing the effects of drugs or surgical lesions on the brain; they are easily established pre-treatment, and give a good index of the behavioral effect of the treatment. Recovery and adaptation may also be investigated. The conditioned response therefore serves as an indicator of the state of the nervous system, and of the neurophysiological processes concerned with behavioral activity. Dimascio et al. (1956) has studied the effects of total body exposure to irradiation, using operant conditioning procedures to evaluate the effects of radiation on behavior. James and McCay (1944) used conditioning techniques to analyze the effects of retarded growth on behavior.

Conditioning of heart rate and motor responses have been studied in relation to cardiovascular conditioning (Mack *et al.*, 1961) experimental psychogenic hypertension (Dykman and Gantt, 1960) and inhibition of urination (Dykman *et al.*, 1962). Recent conditioning experiments employing Pavlovian techniques are being pursued to analyze concepts of schizokinesis, autokinesis and response stereotypy, and a theory of nonavoidance conditioning and extinction regarding conditioning and extinction as emotional learning; also strain and individual differences in conditioning, extinction and extinction under conflict are being analyzed (Dykman, 1964).

Brogden and Gantt (1942) using direct stimulation of the brain established some interesting conditioned responses. A bell conditioning stimulus was given prior to cerebellar stimulation (the unconditioned stimulus). Once conditioning was established, the bell alone would stimulate limb movements resembling cerebellar evoked movements, although the cerebellum was no longer stimulated.

Doty (1961) describes some experiments in the dog where conditioned reflexes were formed and evoked by direct brain stimulation. He found confusing and paradoxical effects; for example, stimulation of the left postcrucial sulcus caused leg raising (and was the U. S.) while the C. S. was derived by stimulating the left suprasylvian gyrus, which caused head movements. Once conditioning had been established, the C. S. became like the U. S. in that the leg was raised following stimulation of the suprasylvian gyrus. Feeding inhibition was obtained by conditioned bar pressing food-reward which was coupled with caudate nucleus stimulation with the unconditioned stimulus of electric shock. Stimulation of the caudate alone will cause feeding inhibition once conditioning is established. Doty observes that there are shifts of excitability in the motor system, several pairings may be required in one stimulated area.

Cook *et al.* (1960) taught dogs to flex their leg to avoid an electric shock, and were later given adrenaline, noradrenaline or acetylcholine thirty seconds before the shock and learned to avoid the shock within the thirty second interval. Injections of saline did not cause withdrawal of the leg so the dogs learned therefore to identify changes in their internal environment (drug-induced) as a signal for performing a learned activity.

References

Allen, W. F.: Effect of bilateral destruction of three lateral cerebral cortical areas on correct conditioned differential responses from general cutaneous stimulation. *Am. J. Physiol., 147*:454-461, 1946.

Anderson, O. D.: See Stockard *et al.*, 1941.

Angermeier, W. F. and James, W. T.: The influence of early sensory-social deprivation on the social operant in dogs. *J. genet. Psychol., 99*:153-158, 1961.

Babkin, B. P.: Experimental neuroses in animals and their treatment with bromides. *Edinburgh Med. J., 45*:605-619, 1938.

Borbrova, M. V.: The rhythmic patellar reflex and types of nervous systems in dogs. *Pavlov J. Higher Nerv. Activity, 11*:3, 1961.

Brogden, W. T. and Gantt, W. H.: Intraneural conditioning: cerebellar conditioned reffexes. *Arch Neurol. & Psychiat., 48*:437-55, 1942.

Chambers, R. M. and Fuller, J. L.: The characteristics of surface and internal temperatures of dogs presented with conditioned and unconditioned stimuli. *J. Comp. Physiol. Psychol., 51*:2:223-226, 1958.

Charles, M. S. and Fuller, J. L.: Developmental study of the EEG of the dog. *Electroenceph. Clin. Neurophysiol., 8*:645-652, 1956.

Cook, L., Davidson, A., Davis D. J. and Kelleher, R. T.: Epinephrine, norepinephrine and acetylcholine. *Science, 131*:990, 1960.

Cornwell, A. C. and Fuller, J. L.: Conditioned responses in young puppies. *J. Comp. Physiol. Psychol., 54*:13-15, 1961.

Dimascio, A., Fuller, J. L., Azrin, N. H., and Jetter, W.: The effect of total-body x-irradiation on delayed-response performance of dogs. *J. Comp. Physiol. Psychol., 49*:600-604, 1956.

Doty, R. W.: Conditioned reffexes formed and evoked by brain stimulation. Chapter 29 in *Electrical Stimulation of the Brain*, D. F. Sheer, ed., University of Texas Press, 1961.

Dukes, H. H.: *The Physiology of Domestic Animals*. Ithaca, New York, Comstock, 1955.

Dykman, R. A.: Personal communication, Medical Center, Univ. Arkansas, 1964.

Dykman, R. A. and Gantt, W. H.: Experimental psychogenic hypertension: blood pressure changes conditioned to painful stimuli (schizokinesis). *Bull. Johns Hopkins Hosp., 107*:2:72-89, 1960.

Dykman, R. A., Corsen, S. A., Reese, W. C. and Seager, L. D.: Inhibition of urine flow as a component of the conditional defense reaction. *Psychosom.*

Med., XXIV:2:177-186, 1962.

Elliot, O. and King, J. A.: Effects of early food deprivation upon later consummatory behavior in puppies. *Psychol. Rep., 6*:391-400, 1960.

Fisher, A. E.: The effects of differential early treatment on the social and exploratory behavior of puppies. Unpublished doctoral thesis, Penn St. Univ., 1955.

Freedman, D. G.: Constitutional and environmental interactions in the rearing of four breeds of dogs. *Science, 127*:585-586, 1958.

Freedman, D., King, J. A. and Elliott, O.: Critical period in the social development of dogs. *Science,* 1016-1017, 1961.

Fuller, J. L., Easler, C. and Banks, E.: The formation of conditioned avoidance responses in young puppies. *Amer. J. Physiol., 160*:462-466, 1950.

Fuller, J. L.: Hereditary differences in trainability of purebred dogs. *J. Genet. Phychol., 87*:229, 1956.

Fuller, J. L., Rosvold, H. E. and Pribram, K. H.: The effect on affective and cognitive behavior in the dog of lesions of the pyriform-amygdala hippocampal complex. *J. Comp. Physiol. Psychol., 50*:89-96, 1957.

Fuller, J. L. and Cornwell, A. C.: Conditioned flexion and cardio-acceleration in the puppy. *Fed. Rec., 18*:198, 1959.

Fuller, J. L., Clark, L. D. and Waller, M. B.: Effects of chlorpromazine upon psychological development in the puppy. *Psychopharmacologica, 1*:393-407, 1960.

Fuller, J. L.: Effects of experimental deprivation upon behavior in animals. *Trans. 3rd World Conference Psychiat.,* Montreal, (1961) 223-227, 1964. U. Toronto Press.

Fuller, J. L.: Effects of drugs on psychological development. *Ann. New York Acad. Sci., 96*:199-204, 1962.

Haley, T. J. and McCormick, W. G.: Intra-cerebral injection of LSD-25 in the unanesthetized dog. *Fed. Proc., 15*:433, 1956.

Himwich, W. A. and Hambrecht, F. T.: Telemetry systems in physiological and pharmacological research. *16th Int. Conf. on Engineering in Medicine and Biology,* 5-7, 1963.

Himwich, W. A., Costa, E. and Himwich, H. E.: Technics for the study of behavior induced by drugs using injections into selected arterial sites in the brain. Acta of the International meeting on the Techniques for the study of psychotropic drugs. Bologna, June. Pub. Modena Soc. Tipograf. Modenese, 1960.

Ivanov-Smolensky, A. G.: *Essays on the Pathophysiology of the Higher Nervous Activity.* Moscow, Foreign Languages Publishing House, ed., 1954.

James, W. T. and McCay, C. M.: An analysis of the effect of retarded growth on behavior in dogs. *J. Comp. Psychol., 37*:3:173-183, 1944.

James, W. T.: Excitable and inhibitable types of dog. *Proc. A. Res. Nerv. & Ment. Dis., 14*:28, 1934.

Krushinski, I. V.: *Animal Behavior.* New York, Consultant Bureau, 1962.

Lawicka, W.: The effect of prefrontal lobectomy on the vocal conditioned reflexes in dogs. *Acta Biologiae Experimentalis, 17*:317-325, 1957.

Lichtenstein, P. E.: Studies of anxiety. Effects of lobotomy on a feeding inhibition in dogs. *J. Comp. Physiol. Psychol., 43*:419-427, 1950.

Mack, R. L., Davenport, O. L. and Dykman, R. A.: Cardiovascular conditioning in dogs. *Amer. J. Physiol., 201*:3:437-439, 1961.

Mirzakarimova, M. G., Stel'makh, L. N. and Troshikhin, V. A.: Directed changes in passive-defensive and investigatory reflexes in ontogenesis. *Pavlov J. Higher Nerv. Activity, 8*:5, 1958.

Nemenov, M. I.: The effect of roentgen ray exposures of the cerebral cortex on the activity of the cerebral hemispheres. *Radiology, 23*:86-93, 1934.

Parry, H. B.: Viral hepatitis of dogs (Rubarth's disease). *Vet. Rec., 62*:559-565, 1950.

Ross, S., Fisher, A. E. and King, D.: Sucking behavior: a review of the literature. *J. Genet. Psychol., 91*:63-81, 1957.

Ross, S. Scott, J. P. Cherner, M. and Denenberg, V. H.: Effects of restraint and isolation on yelping in puppies. *Animal Behavior, 8*:1-5, 1960.

Scott, J. P. and Marston, M. V.: Critical periods affecting normal and maladjustive social behavior in puppies. *J. Genet. Psychol., 77*:25-60, 1950.

Scott, J. P., Vogel, H. H. and Marston, M. V.: Social facilitation and allelomimetic behavior in dogs. I. Social facilitation in a non-competitive situation. II. The effects of unfamiliarity. *Behavior, 2*:121-143, 1950.

Scott, J. P. and Charles, M. S.: Genetic differences in the behavior of dogs: a case of genetic differences magnified by thresholds and by habit formation. *J. Genet. Psychol., 84*:175-188, 1954.

Scott, J. P. and Fuller, J. L.: Experimental exploration of the critical period hypothesis. *Personality, 1*:162-183, 1954.

Scott, J. P.: Critical periods in the development of social behavior in puppies. *Psychosom. Med., 20*:42-54, 1958.

Scott, J. P., Ross, S., Fisher, A. E. and King, D.: The effects of early enforced weaning on sucking behavior in puppies. *J. Genet. Psych., 95*:261-281, 1959.

Scott, J. P. and Fuller, J. L.: Inheritance of seasonal breeding behavior in the basenji (African barkless) dog. *Anat. Rec., 134*:636, 1959.

Scott, J. P. and Pfaffenberger, C. J.: The relationship between delayed socialization and trainability in guide dogs. *J. Genet. Psychol., 95*:145-155, 1959.

Scott, J. P., Fuller, J. L. and King, J. A.: The inheritance of annual breeding cycles in hybrid Basenji-cocker spaniel dogs. *J. Hered., 50*:255-261, 1960.

Scott, J. P. and Elliot, O.: The development of emotional distress reactions to separation in puppies. *J. Genet. Psychol., 99*:3-22, 1961.

Scott, J. P.: Spectrographic analysis of dog sounds. *Amer. Zoöl., 1*:387, 1961.

Scott, J. P.: The process of primary socialization in canine and human infants. *Child Develop. Monographs, 85*:28:1, 1963.

Scott, J. P., Deshaies, D. and Morris, D. D.: The effects of emotional arousal on primary socialization in the dog. *J. Nerv. Ment. Dis.* 1962, in press.

Scott, J. P.: Critical periods in behavioral development. *Science, 138*:949-958, 1962.

Scott, J. P. and Fuller, J. L.: *Genetics & Behavior of the dog.* U. Chicago Press (in preparation).

Speakman, T. F. and Babkin, B. P.: Changes in behavior following frontal lobectomy in dogs and cats. *Arch. Neurol. & Psychiat., 63*:433-443, 1950.

Stanley, W. C.: Differential human handling as reinforcing events and as treatments influencing later social behavior in puppies. *Amer. Phychologist, 13*:388, 1958.

Stanley, W. C. and Elliot, O.: Differential human handling as reinforcing events and as treatments influencing later social behavior in basenji puppies. *Psych. Rep., 10*:775-588, 1962.

Stelmakh, L. N.: Ontogenetic development of external inhibition in the dog. *Pavlov J. Higher Nerv. Activity, 8*:2:216, 1958.

Stockard, C. R., Anderson, O. D. and James, W. T.: Genetic and endocrine basis for differences in form and behavior. *Am. Anat. Mem. No. 19,* Philadelphia, Wistar Inst. Biol., 1941.

Thompson, W. R. and Heron, W.: The effects of early restriction on activity in dogs. *J. Comp. Physiol. Psychol., 47*:1, 77-82, 1954.

Tunturi, A. R.: Effects of lesions of the auditory cortex and adjacent cortex on conditioned reflexes. *Am. J. Physiol., 181*:225-229, 1955.

Waller, M. B. and Fuller, J. L.: Preliminary observations on early experience as related to social behavior. *Am. J. Orthopsychiatry, 31*:254-266, 1961.

Wilker, A.: Adaptive behavior in long-surviving dogs with neocortex. *Arch. Neurol. & Psychat. 66*:29-41, 1951.

Chapter 6

EXPERIMENTALLY INDUCED BEHAVIORAL ABNORMALITIES

S EVERAL WORKERS have experimentally induced "neuroses" in the dog and other animals. The Pavlovian Laboratories initially worked on methods of breakdown depending on the type of nervous system in the individual dog (Ivanov-Smolenski, 1954). Over strain of excitatory and inhibitory processes and "phasic" states of the nervous system were considered factors which may be manipulated by using classical conditioned responses to produce "experimental neuroses."

A single case history of a long-term study of experimental neurosis using Pavlovian conditioning has been reported (Gantt, 1944). The dog was studied for twelve years and over 10,000 conditioned responses were observed in this subject. Significant alterations in autonomic function (digestive, circulatory, respiratory, urinary and sexual) were observed. Heart rate was found to be the most sensitive indicator of CNS excitation. Cardiac conditioned reflexes were formed more rapidly and were less easily extinguished than either bodily activity or salivary secretions. This long-term study established norms of conditionability and reactivity of various autonomic functions. Conditioned cardiac acceleration, for example, may persist for several years after the external stimulus no longer demands excessive changes indicative of a neurotic disturbance: restlessness, increased motor activity, inhibition of conditioned feeding reflexes, disturbed respiration and later frequent micturition and pathologic penile erections were observed.

Present studies are concerned more with the effect of the induced neurosis on function of the body as a whole in relation to stress, the autonomic nervous system, and disease processes. Pavlov's concept was that these experimental neuroses were full analogues of human neuroses but this concept is no longer widely held. Liddell's (1956) studies on sheep by similar conditioning techniques of "overstimulation" reveal that both autonomic and locomotor symptoms are apparent and indicative of the onset of the neurosis, and changes in social behavior may be marked and sustained for several years without further experimental reinforcement. Gantt, a Pavolvian working in this country, investigated what he terms "normal" psychological trauma seen, for example, during parturition, fighting, confinement, and sudden accidental disturbances, as the normal domestic animal might experience. He also studied the disturbances caused by conflict of drives and excitatory and inhibitory stimuli (Gantt, 1944). Massermann (1943) studied especially the monkey and cat and used a psychoanalytical approach for the interpretation of behavior in the laboratory environment. Both laboratory environment and the conditioning stimulus were contributory to the development of a nervous breakdown. Typically, the conditioning stimulus would be a light flash or buzzer followed by a very mild electric shock (the unconditioned stimulus). Repeated stimuli caused breakdowns in some animals while others were resistant. The conditioning stimulus caused a state of "vigilance" or mounting anxiety tension.

The modern approach employed by experimental psychologists will now be outlined, but first mention must be made of attempts by these earlier workers to restore their neurotic animals to normal. The following methods were employed with apparently good results, which may have clinical applications (from Broadhurst, 1960).

1) Completely change the environment and give no further conditioning stimuli.

2) Forcibly place animal near conditioning stimulus (which caused the neurosis) to show the animal that the stimulus will not cause physical injury.

3) Give further stimuli to cause conditioned inhibition.

Figure 1. Approach and avoidance influenced by early experience.

(1961) supports this impression in that maximal socialization was attained between six to seven weeks. After this time, inhibitory mechanisms are superimposed and avoidance is seen, reaching a later peak of intensity at twelve weeks of age. The development of imprinting in the duckling is similar. The first few hours of life are critical for the formation of the following response, but in a short time inhibition occurs and fear responses reach a maximal intensity. This phenomenon would seem to have a survival value to the animal. Innate mechanisms ensure socialization with its own species at a critical or sensitive period. After this time when primary social relationships have been made, inhibition of the generalized response occurs ensuring survival from predators as escape avoidance and fear responses supervene. The importance of this will be discussed in Chapter 9 where age factors critical to the formation of social relationships with man in the domestic environment will be considered.

Treatment of the isolation syndrome to establish socialization was mediated by several techniques involving sedation with chlorpromazine to reduce anxiety, gentle handling and slow introduction to the new environment; i.e., avoidance of overstimulation by controlled manipulation of sensory stimuli (or sensory input) therefore gradually introducing the animal to its surroundings. This last method resembles rehabilitation methods employed in human psychiatry, where re-learning to perform and function in the social environment outside the institution (or outside the experimental situation in the case of the dog) is effected by slow and progressive procedures.

Using conditioning techniques (Fig. 2), problems of learn-

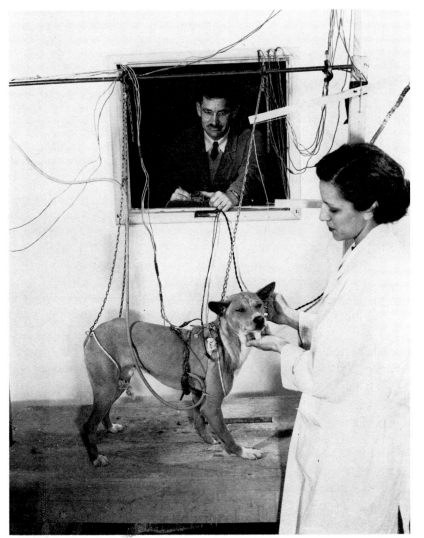

Figure 2. Dog in conditioning harness. (Courtesy Dr. John L. Fuller.)

ing theory may be explored and it frequently happens that during such experiments the animals may develop behavioral abnormalities indicative of an "experimental neurosis." For example, in a study where dogs were trained to jump over an obstacle on receiving an electric shock, it was found that after a short time dogs would jump when a buzzer was sounded prior to the electric shock, therefore establishing a conditioned reflex. Attempts to inhibit this response by putting up a large glass barrier over the jump, or giving an electric shock after the dog had jumped, failed in extinguishing the conditioned response. The dogs actually jumped faster and more vigorously, and urination, panting, yelping, salivation, and stereotyped behavior ("fixation") were seen in different dogs.

It was argued that jumping was reinforced by shock termination during the escape phase, and also by anxiety reduction, but anxiety decreases as the conditioned stimulus response (response to the buzzer) becomes more stereotyped (i.e., shorter latency of response). As long as the conditioned emotional response has not extinguished, each jump after the conditioning stimulus was followed by anxiety reduction. Behavior was therefore adapted to this experimental situation, and as the responses were stereotyped, maladaptive behavior was seen after attempts to cause extinction of the conditioned response had failed.

It was concluded that traumatically acquired habits maintain a marked resistance to extinction despite lack of renewed primary reinforcement. Behavior therefore persists as a neurosis of perpetuating non-adaptive behavior (Solomon *et al.*, 1953).

In other conditioning experiments, designed to produce experimental neurosis, dogs became hyperactive and hyperirritable; pseudo-decerebrate rigidity (the limbs could be passively moved into any position by the experimenter) was seen, and stereotyped behavior, e.g., whirling and insensitivity to pain. Somnolence and anorexia nervosa may arise spontaneously or during "breakdown" in the experimental room.

To review the techniques employed in the production of an experimental neurosis or more properly maladaptive behavior manifest as a conditioned emotional reaction, the following methods have been used effectively in sheep, cats and dogs by earlier workers (Stone, 1952) .

1) Conditioned stimulus presented so as to inhibit a strong inborn reaction and also to establish a new association.

2) Presentation to the animal of similar conditioned stimuli to mutually exclusive behavior.

3) Delay of reinforcement of positive conditioned reactions for a given period of time after the beginning of the conditioned stimuli.

4) Rapid transition from one conditioned stimulus to another stimulus evoking antagonistic behavior.

5) Reinforcement of a conditioned stimulus that previously had an inhibitory effect.

6) Occurrence of very strong or unusual stimuli.

Symptoms: 1) Impairment of discrimination or learning and disturbed behavior in the learning situation. 2) Autonomic disturbances—fear, rage, secretory, sexual, cardiac, digestive, and respiratory changes. Notably in the dog, autonomic changes (inhibition of food-conditioned reflexes, urination, hyperpnea) often occurred before overt behavioral changes are seen.

Accidental disturbances have caused behavioral abnormalities in experimental dogs. Reports of Pavlov's dogs showing bizarre behavior after the Leningrad flood are well documented. Fighting has caused temporarily altered behavior and disruption of conditioned responses. Restriction of freedom in a small cage apparently caused severe diminution of activity in one dog which died after four months. In some cases the spontaneous behavioral disturbance was correlated with the type of nervous system (or emotionality) of the dog, while other experimental dogs similarly exposed to the psychologically traumatic situation were not affected because they were of a different type of emotional constitution (Gantt, 1944) .

Other abnormalities have been seen in dogs reared in social isolation during the critical period of socialization. Approach behavior toward humans is reduced, and avoidance behavior is marked, which is supported by further experiments on the ontogeny of the passive defensive reflex by Russian workers. These animals show irrational fear of inanimate and animated objects and, although they avoid human contact (touch shyness) , they are rarely aggressive, although fear biting occurs. The superficial reflexes, notably the panniculus, are either hyperactive or inhibited, although pain sensitivity may apparently decrease (personal observations).

Dykman and Gantt (1960) reported the pathological behavior of one dog produced by traumatic electrical stimuli observing marked cardiac changes during the orienting response to the conditioning stimulus. Recovery was effected by giving mild, reassuring shocks. Gantt (1944) observes that some cases of psychotic behavior or experimental neurosis can be differentiated into those showing schizokinesis (or a "split" in the formation of the autonomic and motor responses) and autokinesis (independent internal autonomic development without the repetition of stress).

References

Barnett, S. A.: "Displacement behavior" and "psychosomatic" disorder. *Lancet, 2*:1203-1208, 1955.

Broadhurst, P. L.: Abnormal animal behavior. In *Handbook of Abnormal Psychology*, H. J. Eysenk, ed. London, Pitman, Medical, 1960.

Dykman, R. A. and Gantt, W. H.: A case of experimental neurosis and recovery in relation to the orienting response. *J. Psychol., 50*:105-110, 1960.

Freedman, D., King, J. A. and Elliot, O.: Critical period in the social development of dogs. *Science, 133*:1016-1017, 1961.

Gantt, W. H.: *Experimental Basis for Neurotic Behavior: Origin and Development of Artificially Produced Disturbances of Behavior in Dogs.* New York, Hoeber, 1944.

Gantt, W. H.: Principles of nervous breakdown in Schizokinesis and Autokinesis. *Am. N. Y. Acad. Sci., 56*:2, 143-163, 1953.

Hebb, D. O.: Spontaneous neuroses in chimpanzees: theoretical relations with clinical and experimental phenomena. *Psychosom. Med., 9*:3-16, 1947.

Ivanov-Smolensky, A. G.: *Essays on the Pathophysiology of the Higher Nervous Activity.* Moscow, Foreign Languages Publishing House, ed., 1954.

Lichtenstein, P. E.: Studies of anxiety. II. The effect of lobotomy on a feeding inhibition in dogs. *J. Comp. Physiol. Psychol., 43*:419-427, 1950.

Liddell, H. W.: *Experimental Neuroses in Animals and Man.* Thomas, Springfield, Ill., 1956.

Mahl, G. F.: Physiological changes during chronic fear. *Am. N. Y. Acad. Sci., 56*:2, 240-252, 1953.

Massermann, J. H.: *Behavior and Neurosis: an Experimental Psychoanalytic Approach to Psychobiologic Principles.* Chicago, University of Chicago Press, 1943.

Muller, F. L. and Schmidt, H. D.: Psychogenic vomiting in a dog. *Berl.*

Münch. Tierärztl. Wschr., 74:382, 1961.

Solomon, R. L., Kamin, L. J. and Wynne, L. C.: Traumatic avoidance learning: the outcomes of several extinction procedures with dogs. *J. Abnorm. Soc. Psychol., 48*:291-302, 1953.

Stone, C. S.: *Comparative Psychology.* 3rd ed., New York, Staples, 1952.

Chapter 7

SPONTANEOUS BEHAVIORAL ABNORMALITIES RELATED TO EARLY EXPERIENCES AND INHERITANCE

W ITH AN EXPERIMENTALLY orientated approach to the artificial genesis of abnormal behavior in the dog, we must next consider the spontaneous occurrence of abnormal behavior in the domestic pet.

Normal Developmental Background

There is an initial period, the critical period of socialization, which influences the behavior of the dog in later life, followed by a Juvenile period which persists until the onset of sexual activity, breeding, and the rearing of young with associated maternal behavior. The various types of adult behavior patterns have been classified as follows (Scott, J. P., 1962) :

Ingestive; eliminative; sexual; agonistic (aggression and submission, fear, fighting, etc.) ; epimeletic (care giving, e.g., maternal behavior) ; et-epimeletic (care seeking) ; allelomimetic; shelter seeking; investigatory.

Normally a puppy is taken from the litter between five and eight weeks of age and socialized with man in the domestic situation. Frequent contact with people and other animals of the same and different species and familiarization with the environment and associated stimuli (knock on the door, traffic noise, etc.) condition the young puppy to the normal environment of domestication. The behavior of the owner at this time also influences their later relationship; normally the owner is dominant and is the superior in the social heirarchical position which is established between man and dog.

94

Behavioral abnormalities rarely arise under these conditions, where the dog is well oriented and adapated to a comparatively normal domestic environment. However, four factors must be considered.

1) Behavioral change due to an undiagnosed neurological lesion and the symptoms may be incorrectly regarded as behaviorally abnormal.

2) Senescent changes—incontinence, deafness, blindness, and associated decline in manipulative abilities; mild behavioral changes may be associated with increasing age and decreased sensory acuity and awareness.

3) Traumatic experience causing a conditioned emotional reaction is frequently seen in the normally reared dog. A visit to the veterinary surgery may on the second visit result in hyperthermia; fright, fight, and flight mechanisms are brought into play by the emotional arousal of the autonomic nervous system. Vomiting or diarrhea may be seen, or refusal to eat food (anorexia nervosa), if the stimulus causing the fear reactions is a restricted activity (e.g., kennelling in the veterinary hospital). Sedative drugs are effective prophylactic treatment. If these reactions are caused by an object, e.g., irrational fear of an automobile, sedation and gentle handling and restraint to resocialize (or refamiliarize) and teach the dog that the fearful objects are innocuous should be instituted.

4) Genetic and inherited or constitutional factors: inbreeding of certain strains for physical characteristics irrespective of aggressive or hysterical tendencies is common practice among certain breeders. Epilepsy is an inherited disease and both aggression, touch shyness, and timidity may be inherited. The genetic constitution of the animal may so modify its behavior as to make it suitable for only certain activities or adaptable only to certain types of environment. Behavioral restriction may arise under the normal domestic situation, notably in the working sheep dog and gun dogs kept as city pets. It is important therefore that the prospective owner should have a dog that is adaptable to the environment in which it is to be kept; this is often not the case, and sudden aggression towards strangers or children has been observed, or destructive tendencies (displacement activities causing

increased motivation to reduce "boredom" or tension of inactivity) in the household.

Agonistic Behavioral Abnormalities

Disorders may arise due to traumatic experiences during the critical period of socialization, or they may be due to lack of experience (as a result of social isolation) also during this period. Normally the puppy is taken from the litter as a pet at about five to seven weeks of age and this is the time for maximal emotional attachment to man. If they are bought from breeders rearing them until a later age with little human contact, socialization and housebreaking may be almost impossible, as proved experimentally. In cities it is common for puppies to be taken as pets and live a fairly isolated life in an apartment. Socialization with other dogs and people is therefore greatly reduced and the deficit may be even greater if the puppy is taken as a pet from the litter at four weeks of age. Overdependency towards the owner results and the animal is incapable of making positive social relationships with other animals and is a problem when a veterinary examination is required for example. Escape behavior and mass fear responses or fear biting may develop. If the animal becomes dominant (and overprotective) to the owner, as frequently happens in the overindulged pet, the dog may show extreme aggression towards strangers or other dogs, provided it is with its owner or in its own household territory. When separated from these environmental influences this type of dog is often quite easy to handle after initial domination by the handler by scruff-shaking. The overdependent and submissive pet is more likely to develop nervous anorexia when separated and put into boarding kennels. Such an animal responds well to tranquillization, gentle treatment, and hand feeding, which tend to reduce these overfearful responses.

With inability to socialize with other dogs, overdependent dogs socialized too early in life to one person in a restricted environment may be impossible to breed from. Some overindulged animals, because of the care soliciting (and dominant) behavior of the owner, are maintained as et-epimeletic juveniles and may exhibit bizarre behavior during pregnancy in the home, or post-operatively following some time in the veterinary hospital. Sexual behavior towards the owner may also occur in this type of dog, and also toward animals of a different species (Scott, 1961; Hutyra *et al.,* 1947).

Disturbances in the environment may cause emotional arousal and behavior becomes abnormal so as to compensate for the change and act as an anxiety relief mechanism to emotional conflict, e.g., psychogenic vomiting and psychogenic polyphagia.

The other extreme is the underindulged or neglected dog which, reared under social isolation, becomes extremely unstable emotionally and develops overfearful responses towards strangers, resembling autisticism in children. Gentle handling and resocialization is effective but slow treatment for such animals. Aggression is generally weak in these dogs, but fear biting is common when escape is restricted.

During kennelling and isolation from the owner, some dogs are unable to adapt to the unfamiliar environment, restricted socialization and overdependence being etiologically the most probable contributory factors. Anxiety under these circumstances may be expressed in several emotional disturbances involving the autonomic system (i.e., psychosomatic). Diarrhea, anorexia, and vomiting may occur and hyperesthesia to handling (commonly termed touch shyness) and reduced pain threshold, hyperpnoea and cardiac irregularities. Although certain breeds are susceptible to these disorders, it must be remembered that the type of dog is usually chosen by the owner for its own individual nature reputable to the breed and this choice on the owner's part may reflect the needs and behavior of the owner which may directly affect the behavior of the dog independently of inherited factors (Barton, 1958; Speck, 1964) (see Chapter 8).

Et-epimelesis

Frequently a dog may become a child substitute and a symbolic expression for the affections of the owner. Overdependency may arise due to overindulgence, or the animal becomes dominant, again due to overindulgence by the owner, or becomes overprotective toward the owner, and aggressive towards strangers. Here the pet is fulfilling an excellent purpose as a crutch for the emotional and social needs of the owner and the veterinarian has a great moral responsibility to both client and patient in these

cases. The behavior of the dog may mirror the social and emotional state of the owner and the apparently abnormal behavior
of the dog is normal and adaptive to the situations of its home
environment. These animals, however, are very prone to emotional disturbances if they are separated from their owners for
some time, or if there is a change in the home environment (e.g.,
relatives come to visit, and the animal shows extreme aggression
towards them or refuses to eat and develops diarrhea). The veterinarian is frequently confronted with these cases and may not
recognize the behavioral disorder as such, but regards the owner's
overmagnification of the animal's symptoms as characteristic of a
certain type of client and is not surprised when the animal re-
covers on placebo treatment, when no doubt the home environment is again in the original state of equilibrium.

Abnormal Oral and Ingestive Behavior

Compulsive eating and psychogenic vomiting as a result of
emotional conflict will later be described. The chewing and frequent ingestion of small objects is a normal exploratory oral
activity of the young puppy (Rheingold, 1963). In the adult,
however, this may become a vice and the etiology of the disorder,
is hard to ascertain. Pica may suddenly develop in a dog without
previous evidence of disease or contributory factor. Chronic
enteritis is frequently associated with pica. Cases of dogs ingesting
several pounds of gravel or wood shavings and grass may indicate
some alimentary disorder—uremic gastritis or chronic enteritis.
The ingestion of these materials may be designed to cause vomiting and failure to do so result in gastric impaction or occlusion
of the lower bowel in the sick dog. Vomiting in the puppy is
commonly seen and ingested grass and egested Toxocara worms
may point to the fact that grass irritates the gastric mucosa
and facilitates vomiting. Pica and habitual vomiting have been
associated with chronic pharyngitis and chronic tonsillitis. Stone
chewing causing attrition of the teeth (Fig. 1) is a common vice
in the dog and may develop as a true habit rewarded by the activity itself, which may be displacement behavior arising from boredom; i.e., a certain activity becomes hyperactive to compensate for
general inactivity. Similarly destructive tendencies in the house-

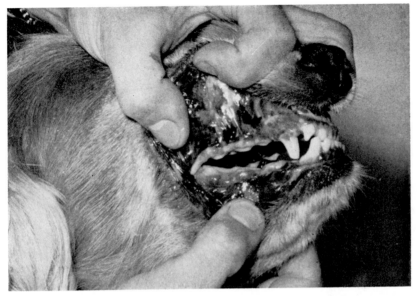

Figure 1. Attrition of teeth in a stone-chewing dog.

hold when the dog is left alone are compensatory displacement activities. Stone chewing may be consummated by ingestion of the object, and these dogs may require enterotomies on several occasions in a lifetime. Deconditioning by inhibitory training would be easier treatment than trying to confine such an animal.

Abnormal Sexual Behavior

Sexual behavior is greatly influenced by the effects of socialization on the animal and has been already well discussed. Inability to breed is frequently seen in dogs that have been overpetted. Sedative drugs may help in mating an excessively nervous bitch. Hormonal imbalances, notably the Sertoli cell tumor, may produce physiological, anatomical, and behavioral feminization in the male, and follicular cysts of the ovaries result in hyperestrinism and nymphomania in the bitch. Masturbation (clasping objects or other dog with the forelimbs and making pelvic thrusts), is a normal activity in the young male at the time of puberty (Barton, 1960). Social hierarchy and dominance greatly influence the consummation of sexual intercourse. Dominant females will

rarely mate with subordinate males. Sexual deviation has been
reported where dogs have been known to attempt copulation with
cats (Scott, 1961) and hens (Hutyra *et al.*, 1937).

A Case History of a socio-sexual behavioral abnormality in
the dog resembling Oedipus complex in man is worth relating.
(Fox 1964).

The subject was an eight year old male golden retriever.
Examination of the external genitalia revealed no abnormalities.
Its entire life was spent with an eleven year old bitch of the same
breed, which was its mother. Both dogs had a free run of the
household and large grounds, which were not enclosed. They in-
frequently roamed outside their territory which was well marked
and defended from neighboring dogs. Judging by their reactions
to their owners, they had been reared normally and were not
overindulged, although submissive behavior was marked in the
presence of strange humans.

The behavior of the two dogs when alone together was observed on several occasions. The male dog (the son) was extremely
submissive toward the bitch (the mother), and would exhibit
et-epimeletic (care seeking) behavior by lying between her fore
feet and stimulating her to lick her face and eyes. This would
continue for a long period of time, but was never reciprocated.
The son was physically larger than the mother, in both weight
and stature, and when playing with a bone or ball exhibited
normal dominance over the mother, including scruff holding and
pinning. Frequent genital exploratory behavior was seen, and the
occurrence of this behavior conformed to no obvious time pattern. The mother had been ovioriohysterectomized after her first
pseudopregnancy five years previously, and subsequently never
showed signs of heat, vulval enlargement or discharge. The son
would also frequently attempt to mount the mother and penile
erection was observed. Attempts to breed this dog with a normal
bitch in estrus failed in the past history, and the owner reported
the dog showed no sexual interest.

Offspring breeding with their parents is common among
domesticated animals, and is frequently used to maintain colonies
of inbred animals for research. In the case presented, however, an
apparently physically normal male dog exhibited sexual behavior

toward his mother only, who was ovariohysterectomized several years previously. Attempts to make this male with normal females failed and this would appear to be the interaction of two factors. Primary is the submissive et-epimeletic behavior of the male toward the dam. Normally the male is aggressive and does not show et-epimelesis after puberty. Secondary is the evidence that the dog is capable of sexual activity, but only with the dam. The interaction of these two factors makes this male behaviorally impotent with strange females, and one may surmise that, because of its social relationship with the dam, a behavioral fixation developed. This may have arisen as a result of "imprinting" during the critical period of sexual behavior at the time of puberty. As both dogs defended their home territory from strange dogs, the young male would not be socialized sexually with other members of its own species. Similarly in dogs that have been kept in restricted socialization in the domestic environment, sexual behavior may be directed toward the owner, and breeding with its own species may be impossible. The condition resembles the oedipus complex in man where it is recognized that during puberty endocrine and psychologic development is at a critical period, when aberrations in psychosocial relationships may cause persistent behavioral changes at the functional (social) level, although physiologic maturity and normal endocrine function is present.

Abnormal Epimeletic Behavior (Fox, 1964)

Cannibalism is a rare occurrence in the dog. One case has been reported in a bitch that was deaf, and it was thought that, as she was unable to hear the pups yelping, she eviscerated them while eating the fetal membranes and chewing through the umbilical cords (McCuiston, 1956). This however may be improbable, for the normal bitch responds more to the pup by visual than auditory cues at partiurition (Bleicher, 1962). Several pups have been seen partially eviscerated, or with considerable skin and abdominal muscles chewed around the umbilicus by the bitch, and those with less severe lesions recover well (personal observations). Cannibalism as it is recognized in rodents (King, 1963) probably does not exist in the canine species. Similar accidental cannibalism, comparable to the dog, has been reported in primiparous lions (Cooper, 1942).

Normal aggression, punishment, scattering and desertion of the litter have been described in Chapter 3. Extreme aggression may occur at the time of weaning when the pups are eating solid food and the mother competes for the same feed dish. This has been observed in one cocker spaniel who attacked the offspring of two successive litters. All pups developed subcutaneous bite-abscesses on the top of their heads. The wounds were inflicted solely in this region.

Sudden changes in the environment may disrupt innate patterns of maternal behavior. Surroundings should be quiet and undisturbed during parturition. Maternal rejection has been seen (Whitney, 1960) after experimental abortion. Bitches who delivered before the fifty-sixth day ignored their first-born puppies and walked away from them. Only toward the end of parturition did they begin licking the later-born pups. Bitches who delivered at the fifty-eighth day or later behaved normally.

Abnormal Allelomimetic Behavior

This behavior is normally only seen where large numbers of dogs are housed together and abnormally in dogs reared singly in close confinement (see Fig. 2). Hyperactivity (weaving, circling, and whirling) is characteristic and is probably adaptive to the situation for the condition arises as a result of too long confinement. Exercise, larger pens, and frequent pen changes to new localities tend to reduce these stereotyped activities arising from thwarted allelomimetic behavior. Certain breeds are more prone to the development of these displacement activities than are others. Whirling behavior in dogs as related to early experience has been reported by Thompson et al. (1956) (see Figs. 2 and 3).

Senescence

With increasing age the animal becomes more dependent upon its home environment and any disturbances may give rise to changes in behavior. Loss of auditory and visual acuity, and decreased motor efficiency are usually well compensated and it is surprising that old dogs may remain dominant animals in the social hierarchy of the neighborhood. Senile incontinence is an unfortunate disability and usually terminates relationships with

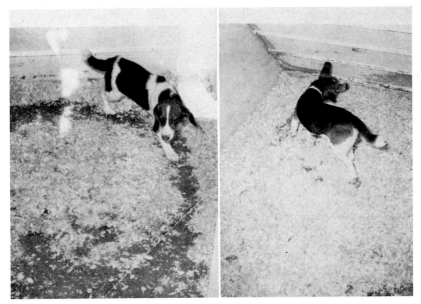

Figure 2. Pacing and whirling displacement activities, as a result of early confinement.

the owner. Chronic encephalitis and tumors occur more in older dogs and the general incidence of neurogenic behavioral disorders increases with age.

Unexpected Psychological Trauma

Fight, fright, and flight mechanisms are in part mediated through the autonomic nervous system and sudden environmental stimuli calling forth these mechanisms may produce a state of shock, varying in severity and duration. When represented with the same stimuli the animal may (by learning) adapt to the situation or under repetitive stimulation develop bizarre behavior, mass fear responses, and undue aggression, indicative of maladaptive behavior. If such responses are directed towards an object (e.g., train noise) or person, gradual resocialization and restraint may be possible by teaching the animal that the fearful objects are innocuous. Sedation may be employed if the stimulus causing fear reactions is a restricted activity (e.g., car journey or visit to the veterinary hospital), where no avoidance or escape is possible.

Genetic Considerations

Mention has already been made of the suitability of a certain breed of dog to the environment in which it is to live and activities it is expected to perform. Although many behavior traits are acquired under environmental stimuli, heredity may cause a diathesis towards the precipitation of abnormal behavior. Some breeds are naturally less active than others and are more sociable, while others are hyperactive and individualistic. Aggression, fear biting, touch shyness, and epilepsy are frequently found in certain strains of dog as inherited differences in the "type" (balance or emotionality) of the nervous system.

Compulsive Behavior Disorders

Behavioral disorders arising from conflict situations have been produced experimentally in the dog by several workers. The resultant behavior may be persistent, or occur only when the conflict situation is represented.

Under everyday circumstances conflict situations may arise during the life of the pet dog and maladaptive behavioral responses may be recognized. Abnormal aggression towards owners or other animals has been reported in dogs under emotional conflict. These dogs are generally very intelligent and sensitive to the reactions and behavior of their owners. A case of psychogenic vomiting in a dog in a similar conflictual emotional state has been described and the following case history of similar etiology is presented (Fox, 1962).

The dog was a twelve-year-old male Welsh terrier and had been the only pet of the household for several years. It was an over-indulged, fear-biting dog. Earlier in its life attempts had been made to "socialize" the dog with cats, but all attempts had failed.

It was then suggested to the owners, who still wanted a cat, that a young farm cat should be used as a "Kumpan" relation for the dog on the assumption that the young cat had no experience of being chased by a dog and so would not release the chase response of the dog (Spurway, 1953). The dog was restrained on first being introduced to the cat as it had been conditioned to give chase on seeing one, cats acting as a sign stimulus for the chase response. At the cat did not flee, the initial restraint of the dog by the owner and the negative stimulus response (i.e., no "flee" response) from the cat, negated the chase response of the dog.

On the third day after the initial period of socialization the dog could be left unattended with the young cat. Over a period of ten weeks a "Kumpan" relationship between the dog and the cat was established so that social dominance or submission became dependent upon the territory occupied by the respective animals at different times. Aggression and nervous anorexia marked the introductory period of socialization, which lasted three days. After this time the dog could be left alone with the cat. It tended to remain in its basket and growl if the cat came near (agonistic or aggressive territorial defensive behavior). Et-epimeletic (care-soliciting) behavior was greatly increased when the owner was present.

The dog was normally given an evening meal of scraps and tinned meat and a day's supply of biscuits in the morning which it would eat at leisure. On the fourth day the dog began to empty its bowl of biscuits (a full day's supply) and this would be refilled by the owner to prevent any jealousy when the cat was fed. The procedure of *ad lib.* feeding continued until the dog was consuming five times its normal amount of food. Vomiting and flatus were constant features following rapid ingestion of the food. At six weeks the dog was grossly oversize and compulsive eating continued when the dog was fed in the presence of the cat. On no occasion did the cat attempt to eat from the same bowl: the dog would not allow the cat near it during feeding.

It was felt that a simple remedy would be effective if the dog was fed at the same time as the cat, but given a restricted diet: conflict would then be reduced, and the physiological disturbances of eating too much and too quickly would be overcome. Neither animal was to be petted by the owner, so as to reduce et-epimeletic responses and further emotional conflict during feeding.

After two weeks, compulsive eating was no longer evident, although the dog tended to eat faster in competition with the cat (normal social facilitation). A full day's supply of biscuits could be left for the animal to consume at leisure.

After this period, socialization was complete and no further behavioral abnormalities were recorded.

Compulsive eating is a recognized psychogenic disorder of man (Glanzmann, 1952). Differential diagnosis of polyphagia, including metabolic disorders, e.g., diabetes mellitus, atrophic pancreatitis and nutritional deficiency diseases, must be considered and eliminated before a definite diagnosis of maladaptive behavior or psychogenic disorder can be established.

In this case a conflict situation arose where et-epimeletic behavior towards the owner and ingestive and appetitive behavior in the presence of the cat became maladaptive. The et-epimeletic behavior became competitive to the same behavior of the cat towards the owner, so that in the presence of food an association was established with resultant maladaptive ingestive behavior of psychogenic origin. Compulsive eating followed and may be regarded as a form of displacement behavior, or anxiety relief mechanism to a conflict situation epistatic to its instinctive behavior.

Although clinically this case was easily treated and in such a light may seem trivial, common sense on the part of the owner is the best prophylaxis. Such cases are worthy of recording for the fuller understanding of animal behavior and inter-species relationships.

Segall (1964) has reported an interesting case of opium addiction in the dog, where the owners established a routine of giving the dog an opium containing drug (paragoric: camphorated tincture of opium) before they retired for the evening. The dog would not settle unless it was given this attention, and eventually developed symptoms of morphine intoxication. In such a case, where a routine was established between dog and owner, it was difficult to break the routine to which the dog was accustomed, and it is debatable whether the dog was addicted to the drug itself or to the rewarding routine attention.

Another psychogenic disorder has been reported in the dog (Muller and Schmidt, 1962). In this case, the dog vomited at night and it was thought that this was due to the dog wanting companionship because it was locked in isolation throughout the night. In the morning the owners would give the dog extra attention, therefore reinforcing the condition which developed as a result of social deprivation. Vomiting ceased when the dog was removed from this particular domestic environment. Ethologically orientated experiments have produced psychogenic vomiting in the controlled laboratory environment.

Submissive Paw Raising and Sympathy Lameness (Fox, 1962)

Paw raising in the dog is seen as a normal response to social stimuli, or may be observed out of context where no clinico-pathological lesion can be found. Here the behavior may be regarded as aberrant in itself. Further clinical examination and details of past history and experience may help in ascertaining the etiology of sympathy lameness in some instances, where pain may or may not be evident. Often the leg may be carried when the animal is standing, but used normally when running or occupied in tracking or pursuing.

Normal forepaw raising is first seen in the puppy in response to licking by the bitch during the process of litter cleaning. This response may be seen from as early as three weeks of age, and the animal later develops the "follow-through" of lateral recumbency and raising of the uppermost hind limb. This activity pattern persists and is especially evident at the pre-pubertal and pubertal stages of development. Forepaw raising has been described together with tail-wagging and licking as et-epimeletic (care soliciting) behavior, being an early social response towards both litter mates and complete strangers, and appearing as early as the fourth week of life. As a social behavior pattern it becomes reinforced during aggressive and submissive play until definite socially dominant or submissive individuality is evolved.

After paw raising and the follow-through to recombency and hind leg raising adolescent dogs may then urinate, as an act of submission to the owner or to the socially dominant dog. Punishment after urination in these circumstances would not be understood by the dog who was, after all, only being deferential (Worden, 1959).

Similarly, forepaw raising, and the sequence of postural changes often terminating with urination, is seen in submissive bitches especially during estrus, and in timid, socially inferior adult males. In the anti-social, fear-biting or fear-aggressive animal, forepaw raising provides a rapid means of escape, modifying the position to one of submission. This is frequently seen in nervous dogs afraid of strangers, and the cause in many cases may be due to

a severe traumatic psychological experience occurring at some
stage of puppyhood during the critical period of socialization.
Highly nervous strains have an inherited diathesis for this condition.

Nervous dogs under emotional stress (anxiety) may show
the same behavior pattern; here paw raising is reinforced by
stimuli causing anxiety reduction responses such as recumbent
submission, nervous licking (lips, genitals, furniture), urination
and barking. Confusion and displacement activities may follow.

Paw raising is often wrongly encouraged by the owner by too
frequently evoking begging responses from the puppy. In later
life this may become a domestic nuisance when the dog insists on
a complete follow-through of behavior to engage in play, submissive urination, or clasping with the forelimbs to perform copula-
tory movements. These activities are habitually conditioned responses and are very difficult for the owner to abolish.

Certain groups of dogs, therefore, show considerable variation
of the paw-raising response, according to the type of socio-
environmental stimulus or association of effective conditions, and
also according to their previous experience of these conditions in
relation to their present emotional constitution, age and activity;
breed-type and strain variability are both important factors, as
already indicated. The response disappears with maturity in the
majority of dogs, but over-indulged or socially-maladjusted animals may show either permanent or low threshold responsiveness.
Full follow-through to urination or displaced sexual activities
present a problem after mismanagement, so that corrective training from an early age is essential.

Paw raising, recumbency, urination, defecation and mounting nervous tension is common in fear-biting dogs being examined
by strangers. Under anxiety or emotional stress, paw raising is at
times seen as lameness, sudden in onset, the paw being raised and
the animal apparently hypersensitive to pain stimuli in this area.
Invariably there is a history of past experience of pain in this area
due to trauma or infection. The animal therefore remembers the
site of pain, and assumes this regressive displacement behavior,
conditioned by reward-sympathy of the owner. This psychogenic
lameness may persist as long as the environmental conditions

provide sufficient stimulus, and, as long as no distracting stimuli are superimposed, should the latter prevail the animal soon becomes normal, and has no abnormality in gait or posture. Paw raising and sympathy lameness are common in petted dogs; if trodden on by the owner, early conditioning to reward-sympathy following a mild foot injury causes the dog to limp in later life to slightest traumatic provocation, although the site of injury is remote from the apparent lameness now presented. This condition may originate from early et-epimeletic behavior to the owner. It is a problem notable in the toy breeds following orthopedic operations; the animal refuses to use the limb, even when healing is complete, and conditioning reward-sympathy maintains the posture of lameness. Lack of use and poor muscle tone produce a vicious circle of disuse atrophy, fibrosis and contracture. After traumatic nerve lesions, where reflex examination indicates good recovery the patient may refuse to use the affected limb. Habit, lack of confidence or conditioning by sympathy are three important factors involved, either singly or together, and maintain persistent carrying of the limb.

Under emotional stress, therefore, or systemic debility, the dog may limp on a limb on which it was once clinically lame. These cases of reversed fixation or displacement behavior must be differentiated from exacerbations of old limb lesions and progressive, recurrent and sometimes "shifting" arthritis. Estrus and pregnancy, as normal stress factors, are associated frequently with organic lameness, and exacerbations of old lesions due to the relaxation of ligaments and osteoporosis.

Past-associated anxiety due to the direct effect of the limb lesion, and not involving et-epimeletic behavior, may also cause non-specific, "idiopathic" or "psychological" lameness, when conditions produce environmental stimuli similar to the circumstances of the original conditioning experience. The animal, as in previous conditions already described, reverts to a similar state of behavior once the present circumstances are arranged so that the original experience is recalled.

In the clinical differential diagnosis, where no osseous or articular lesions are present, full reflex examination should be carried out, and nerve lesions looked for. Thrombosis, and "re-

mote" effects of constipation, pyometra (toxic neuritis?) and
senescent lumbo-sacral plexus degeneration, apart from traumatic
and infectious spinal cord lesions, are considered in hind-limb
raising or paresis. Hyperesthesia of one forelimb has been attributed to cervical disc lesions. This is not a true case of referred
pain, because the patient only resents movements and manipula-
tions; the limb is carried to prevent movement causing pressure
changes transmitted to tissues surrounding the nerves in the
cervical region, when pain is experienced. Here leg raising is a
protective mechanism. Lameness with suspected angina pectoris
has been noted by several clinicians.

The hind-leg raising action on the male prior to urination,
and clasp response of copulation have not been included in detail
here, as they are separate activities and their development not
related to fore-paw raising and associated submission (see Chapter
3). Clasping activities and precocial sexual behavior have been
observed in puppies as early as four weeks of age when playing.
Forepaw raising in adult dogs when showing aggression, and
which are of equal social status, often assumes a mimetic pattern;
the paw may be placed on the adversary, who may in turn do like-
wise. "Boxing" may ensue, but biting more rarely. The development of this bilateral form of paw raising without submission
can be followed from litter play to the sexual and territorial
behavior of adults.

Observations on submissive leg raising may aid the diagnosis
of behavioral abnormality in some cases. A previously submissive
or timid patient may show sudden aggression without the fear-
aggressive forepaw raising. Both feet are firmly planted and the
whole posture is one of aggression without social or owner awareness. Similar psychic changes have been reported as a sequel to
cerebral trauma, where scar contraction may cause temperamental
changes (McGrath, 1956). Identical changes have been observed
shortly after severe road accidents, and with chronic debilitating
disease and senescence; they are rarely reversible, except in those
cases where there is a definite pain focus, which may eventually
disappear. Relapses can occur in these reversible types, especially
where there is conditioning by the owner to reward-sympathy, or
where conditions arise which recall similar circumstances when a
sudden change of temperament occurred.

In man, comparable psychogenic condition known as hysterical lameness is recognized (Eysenk, 1960). The condition has been seen especially in children where lameness may develop as a result of anxiety or emotional conflict.

Chertok and Fontaine (1963) have recently discussed psychosomatics in veterinary medicine. They cite examples of collective epilepsy, post emotional neuroses (conditioned or perpetuated autonomic arousal) asthmatic-like broncho-spasm, anorexia, dermatitis, enuresis and endocrine disturbances affecting sexual activities. Suggested therapeutic measures for appropriate cases include sedation, and change of environment to modify depressive behavior by bringing back an object or person whose disappearance frustrated the animal. Success of a genuine relational psychotherapy is emphasized, where corrective measures are employed to treat or control organic and functional disturbances which occur as a result of situational stress arising from alterations in interpersonal relationships. Changes in this relationship or situation may cure the animal. Some animals, like different individual human beings, react to stress or conflicts by behavioral change and others by somatic or functional disturbances.

Differential Diagnosis

Inherited and acquired abnormalities of the central nervous and endocrine systems may give rise to abnormal behavior, but it is not within the scope of this book to cover this field in detail. It is however important to be aware of possible disease affecting these systems in the differential diagnosis of abnormal behavior and true psychogenic disturbances. The following more common diseases are listed (p. 112) together with a short account of the symptoms that may be encountered (see *Canine Medicine* (1961) for further details).

Misleading results may come from researchers using pound dogs of obscure origin for experimentation. Chronic disseminating encephalophathies from poorly managed stocks and congenital anomalies from inbred strains, eg. otocephaly, may not be recognized, much to the detriment of the experiment (Fox, 1964). Fortunately this condition of octocephaly was recognized and the strain was eliminated from the breeding stock of experimental animals.

Central Nervous System
Neoplasia (Palmer, 1960).
Trauma and hemorrhage.
(Rabies, Distemper).
Infections and allergic encephalitis.
Senescent changes (chronic
encephalopathies).
Toxic and uremic encephalopathies.

Nutritional
Hypoglycemia.
Hypocalcemia.
Avitaminosis **B** (ageine poisoning).

Congenital
Idiopathic epilepsy
(Eberhart, 1959).

Vestibulocerebellar ataxia.

Hydrocephaly.
Deafness, (bilateral atrophy of the
auditory nerve).
Retinal degeneration.
Octocephaly with hydrocephaly and
temporal lobe reduction.
Endocrine
Pancreatitis (chronic).
Hypothyroidism.
Congenital absence of ovaries or
testicles and eunuchoidism.
Hermphroditism (with ovario-
testis).
Testicular tumor (sertolicell).

Cystic ovaries (follicular).
Pituitary tumor (often without CNS
symptoms).
Diabetes mellitus.

Miscellaneous
Birth anoxia

Gastric irritation, uremic gastro-
enteritis, parasitic or chronic
enteritis.

Symptoms
Symptoms vary as to the location and
extent of the lesion. Changes at the
emotional (psychic) level are especially seen in lesions of the fore-brain,
where extreme aggression, somnolence,
hyperactivity (running fits and psychomotor epilepsy of distemper) may
be seen.
General hyperactivity or hyperirrita-
bility, coma, anorexia, pica, polyphagia.
Running fits, hysteria, paraplegia,
coma.
Symptoms
Symptoms may resemble petit mal fits
or psychomotor epilepsy. There is evidence that this is inherited.
Compulsive circling occurs toward the
affected side.
Retarted neuro-ontogenesis.
Compensatory increase in olfactory and
visual activities.
Progressive loss of visual ability.
In "low grade" forms, petit mal epilepsy develops in early adulthood.

Polyphagia, steatitis, coprophagia.
Obesity, lethargy.
Deficit in sexual behavior.

Deficit in sexual behavior or variable
sexual activities.
Feminization in the male, less aggressive; attract male dogs.
Nymphomania with hyperestrinism.
Adrenogenital syndrome; gynecomasia,
feminization, obesity.
Diabetes insipidus, polydipsia. Hypoglycemia. Hyperirritable, aggressive.
Somolence. Coma.
Symptoms
As yet no case has been reported, although several instances, where after
prolonged parturition the pups develop poorly and show neurologic symptoms similar to anoxia in the human,
have been suspect.
Vomiting, pica (ingestion of foreign
bodies).

Pavlov has described the behavior of dogs with different types of nervous activity. Speaking of dogs with a weak type of nervous system (cited by Krushinskii, 1962) Pavlov states: "We must recognize a type of weak animal, characterized by obvious weakness of both stimulation and inhibition, never fully adapted to life and easily overwhelmed, quickly and often becoming ill or neurotic under the influence of difficult situations in life, or, what amounts to the same thing, during our difficult nervous experiments. The most important factor of all is that this type, as a rule, cannot be greatly improved by training and discipline, and can successfully adapt only in certain particularly favorable, deliberately created conditions or, as we usually call it, in 'hot house conditions." The importance of the strength of the nervous system in the animal's life is clearly seen from this quotation, and Pavlov recognized early in his studies that certain dogs were susceptible to behavior breakdown, while others having a different (stronger and more balanced) type of nervous activity were more resistant and resilient and showed good behavioral adaptation. Pavlov did extensive studies on the typology of the nervous system on different canine subjects, and it is clear that great variance in the "nervous make-up" of present day dogs exists, as indeed do physical, genetic, endocrine and early experience factors differ in their balance, total effect and expression in individual animals. Some individuals, because of the interaction of detrimental innate (inherited) and acquired (experiential) factors, are more prone to behavioral abnormality; poor adaptation (or inability to learn) is maladaptive and perpetuates as a "fixated" abnormal trait, which expresses the inability of the animal to modify its behavior and adapt normally when exposed to unfamiliar stimuli and sudden changes in the environment.

In conclusion, what is to be diagnosed as abnormal behavior should be typically maladaptive to the situation and on a theoretical basis fulfill Hebb's criteria. The clinician should assess the breed background of the animal, its home environment, and any sudden disruption in this environment altering the animal's daily routine behavior or social relationships. If possible, the relationship of animal to owner and vice versa should also be investigated, i.e., overdependency with overindulgence. A thorough past history is important and as relevant in the diagnosis of a behavioral disorder as in the diagnosis of an organic disease. At what age of puppyhood was the dog first acquired; had the animal previous owners or a history of earlier behavioral abnormalities, abnormal estrus cycles, or treatment for organic disease. After initial case history inquiries, some dogs may be handled better if the owner is asked to leave the room; other dogs need heavy tranquillization before presentation to avoid extreme aggression or fear biting; such treatment is often employed to allay nervous anorexia when the dog is brought in for boarding. It must be remembered that the pet dog may adapt to the abnormal behavior of the owner or abnormal home environment and in the eyes of the client, the dog is a perfectly normal creature.

References

Barton, A.: The neurotic pet owner: the medical implications in veterinary practice. *Phila. Med.*, *54*:647-651, 1958.

Barton, A.: Sex abnormalities in the dog and cat. *Vet. Med.*, *55*:11, 1960.

Bleicher, N.: Behavior of the bitch during parturition. *J. Am. Vet. M. A.*, *140*:1076-1082, 1962.

Canine Medicine. By 47 authors. Santa Barbara, California, Veterinary Publications, Inc., 1962.

Chertok, L. and Fontaine, M.: Psychosomatics in veterinary medicine. *J. Psychosom. Res.*, *7*:229-235, 1963.

Cooper, J. B.: An exploratory study of African lions. *Comp. Psychol. Monogr.*, *17*:91:1-48, 1942.

Eberhart, G. W.: Epilepsy in the dog. *Gaines Veterinary Symposium*, New York, 1959.

Eysenk, H. J.: *Handbook of Abnormal Psychology.* London, Pitman Medical, 1960.

Fox, M. W.: Psychogenic polyphagia (compulsive eating) in a dog. *Vet. Rec.*, *74*:38:1023-1024, 1962a.

Fox, M. W.: Observations on paw raising and sympathy lameness in the dog. *Vet. Rec.*, *74*:33, 895-896, 1964.

Fox, M. W.: A socio-sexual abnormality in the dog resembling the Oedipus complex in man. *J. Amer. Vet. M. A.*, *144*:8, 863-869, 1964.

Fox, M. W.: Maternal Aggression in the dog. *Vet. Rec.* *76*:754, 1964.

Fox, M. W.: The otocephalic syndrome in the dog. *Cornell Vet.*, *LIV*, 2:250-259, 1964.

Freud, S.: *The Basic Writings of Sigmund Freud.* A. A. Brill, ed., New York, Modern Library, 1938.

Glanzmann, E.: *Collis's Textbook of Pediatrics.* London, Heinemann, 1952.

King, J. A.: Maternal behavior in *Peromyscus*. In *Maternal Behavior,* H. L. Rheingold, ed., New York, J. Wiley & Sons, Inc., 1963.

McCuiston, W. R.: Puerperal cannibalism in the bitch. *North Am. Vet.,* *37*:862-865, 1956.

McGrath, J. T.: *The Neurologic Examination of the Dog.* London, Kimpton, 1956.

Muller, F. L. and Schmidt, H. D.: Psychogenic vomiting in a dog. *Berl. Münch. Tierärztl. Wschr., 74*:382, 1961.

Palmer, A. C.: Clinicopathologic features of CNS tumors. *Res. Vet. Sci., 1*:36, 1960.

Rheingold, H. L.: Maternal behavior in the dog. Chapter 5 in *Maternal Behavior,* H. L. Rheingold, ed., New York, J. Wiley Sons, Inc., 1963.

Scott, J. P.: Animal sexuality. In *Encyclopedia of Sexual Behavior.* A. E. Ellis and A. Abarbenel, eds., New York, Hawthorn, 1961.

Scott, J. P.: Introduction to animal behavior. Chapter 1 in *The Behavior of Domestic Animals,* E. S. E. Hafez, ed., London, Balliere, Tindall Cox, 1962.

Segall, S.: A case of opium addiction in the dog. *J. Amer. Vet. M. A., 144*:6, 603-604, 1964.

Speck, R. V.: Mental health problems involving the family, the pet, and the veterinarian. *J. Amer. Vet. M. A.,* 145:2:150-154, 1964.

Spurway, E.: Escape drive in the cat, and dog and cat relationships. *Behavior, 5*:81, 1953.

Thompson, W. R., Melzack, R. and Scott, T. H.: "Whirling behavior" in dogs as related to early experience. *Science, 123*:3204:939, 1956.

Whitney, L. F.: Further studies on the effect of Malucidin on pregnancy. *Vet. Med., 55*:57, 1960.

Worden, A. N.: Normal and Abnormal Behavior in the Dog. *Vet. Rec., 71*: 966, 1959.

Chapter 8

TRAINING AND THE PSYCHOSOCIAL RELATIONSHIPS BETWEEN MAN AND DOG

Socialization and Human Relationships

THE PSYCHOSOCIAL PROCESSES involved in primary socialization in the dog have been compared with the human infant, and it is remarkable how similar development is between these two subjects (Scott, 1963). In the restricted environment of domestication the young pup is usually taken from its litter between six to eight weeks of age, which is the optimum time for socialization with man. Abnormalities may arise, however, if the pup is removed from the litter at an earlier age, and reared under semi-isolation away from strange dogs and humans (see Chapter 6). Normally the dog develops in a domestic situation which ensures maximal socialization with a wide variety of species, but restriction occurs especially in dogs reared in city apartments. These dogs may have behavioral deficits such as aberrant sexual behavior; the sexual behavior may be displaced and directed toward the owner and not to its own species, or under restricted socialization may be directed toward an animal of a different species (Scott, 1961). Often the dog is kept as a perpetual juvenile, for the owner stimulates and maintains et-epimeletic behavior by overindulgence. This may act as a form of dominance over the animal, where the owner is hierarchically superior. Conversely, the animal may assume a hierarchically superior position and show extreme agression toward the owner strangers.

Corrective training of these abnormally socialized animals may be difficult; few dog training centers are equipped to deal with these more unusual cases. House breaking may be an initial problem if the pup is taken into the home at a much later age after the optimum age for socialization. The greater effort required to housebreak an older dog may be due to rigidity of behavior which forms after a period of plasticity or trainability, when inhibitory and excitatory processes are balanced. There may be critical phases of development, when the organization of perceptual and behavior patterns pass through phases when they are very plastic (easily influenced) and at a later age are more rigid. Bowlby (1953) has discussed this in a comparative account of critical phases in the development of social responses in man and animals. Maternal separation in man may give rise to several behavioral abnormalities. For example, if a child becomes blind or deaf after four years of age, and is later treated to restore perceptual loss, recovery is good. If, however, there is perceptual loss at birth which is corrected later in life, early perceptual learning has not taken place, and recovery is protracted as early experience has been denied. Separation from parents at six months to three years of age alters social perception and responses, and the child may become "loveless" without attachment to any particular person. Similar cases have been seen in young dogs kept in kennels for a long period of boarding or quarantine. Undirected aggression toward people and inanimate objects (rage-like fits) have been seen in an adult dog that had been placed in isolation during this critical period of socialization. Tail wagging in the pup and the smile response in the child develop at an early age and are generalized responses; later they become specific toward close social relatives. Generalization and then inhibition of these mechanisms therefore takes place during development. This phenomenon resembles imprinting in birds; sexual imprinting also occurs, and birds have been imprinted on man and have been known to exhibit courting behavior toward humans.

Training

Traumatic experience or lack of experience (isolation) or training during a critical period may make it difficult to establish a particular behavior pattern later in life. Bed wetting in children is a good example of this (Bowlby, 1953). At a certain age the child is easily toilet trained, but, if this critical or sensitive time is missed, training is more difficult. Housebreaking a pupy follows a similar pattern.

Generally corrective training in the adult dog is rarely required. However, undesirable habits including destructive tendencies, coprophagia, barking and aggression toward visitors may require treatment. Most training techniques use applied (Pavlovian) conditioning (Merrill, 1945). An unconditioned stimulus (mild electroshock, a light blow on the head with a rolled-up newspaper, or a short jerk on a choke-chain around the neck) is preceded by a command such as "Down" or "No." After several trials, association occurs between the conditioned and unconditioned stimuli so that after the conditioning stimulus the unconditioned stimulus is anticipated. Eventually the unconditioned stimulus can be omitted and the dog will then respond to the conditioned stimulus alone "on the word of command."

Training may be impossible in other circumstances. To allay nervous aggression, anorexia nervosa and other behavioral abnormalities arising from anxiety (the conditioned emotional reaction to, for example, a visit to the veterinary clinic or boarding kennels,) sedatives may be used effectively in some cases. Chlorpromazine has been used experimentally and has been found to cause anixety reduction.

Two interesting cases of aggression occurred in the domestic environment which are worth relating (Pettit, 1962). The first subject was an adult Cocker Spaniel and was reared from an early age by two owners, the husband and the wife. During the day the husband was away at work and the wife gave much attention to the dog. When the husband returned in the evening, her attention was directed toward her husband and the dog was ignored. Eventually the dog became aggressive toward the husband and would attack him when he returned from work. This extreme case of jealousy was cured by advising the husband and wife to give the dog attention as soon as the husband returned from work. Aggression disappeared and the dog soon became adapted to the situation and a stable social hierarchy was established. Similar behavior has been observed in groups of kenneled dogs, where one dog may attack another that is being given human attention. Such cases resemble 'affection hunger' in man. The second case developed in a dog that would bite its owner every time the telephone rang. The cause of this was not ascertained, but effective remedy was obtained by kenneling the dog and ringing an electric bell at frequent intervals; the dog learned that the noise was innocuous.

Training and Special Behavior

The dog is unique among animals in the extent to which learning can be motivated by simple rewards, i.e., a word of praise or body contact from the owner. Early socialization facilitates training because without early experience, rigidity in responsiveness to human handling, training, and reward is encountered. Overstimulization during early training is to be avoided. Theoretically, and reinforced by experimental evidence, increasingly harder tasks result in a conditioned increase in drive to achieve success; suddenly efficiency may decrease and activity increase, indicating the onset of the experimental neurosis; hyperactivity, frustration, agitation, reversed displacement behavior, and inability to perform previously simple activities are seen.

Although environment and human handling influence the animal's efficiency to perform certain tasks, selection on a genetic basis for both psychological and physiological suitability has been undertaken for many generations to give a wide variety of work dog that can perform selected activities under extremes of environmental conditions. Tracking and herding behavior may be bred selectively but further training, which is a specialist occupation, requiring great skill and patience (Pfaffenberger, 1947). Such training, and indeed selection and schooling of guide dogs for the blind, police dogs, and gun dogs, involves applied techniques which are now being investigated under controlled laboratory conditions and a firmer basis established for future and better results. The effects of delayed socialization and trainability of guide dogs have been studied (Pfaffenberger and Scott, 1959) and it was concluded that early training when the dog is a young pup produces better adult dogs to perform special tasks than those where training commences at a later age.

Suitability of Certain Breeds

Finally, a word on the selection of a certain breed as a domestic pet by the owner. Frequently, for psychological reasons (a symbolic expression of the needs of the owner, or repressions, or merely as an outlet for pleasure or social status value) a person will select a dog totally unsuitable for life in a particular domestic environment and although early socialization may help in overcoming this problem, genetic constitutional factors may interact with the environment and give rise to abnormalities in behavior. Boredom, destructive tendencies in the household, and aggressive behavior are commonly seen in working breeds confined to the household, and behaviorial instability and unreliability towards children and strangers. More prospective dog owners should seek veterinary advice, and this should be available, on the selection of a suitable breed. Public demands and changes in fashion from one breed to another result in the emergence of congenital abnormalities, both anatomical and behavioral (notably fear biting, agonistic behavior, and idiopathic epilepsy), as a result of intensive breeding to fulfill the needs of the public. Such problems occur in districts where one breed becomes popular and is bred intensively and distributed throughout that neighborhood. In spite of the emergence of these abnormalities in such strains, the public is slow to realize this, and the veterinarian can help to advise and control the dissemination of such inferior animals.

Psychological Studies of Man-Dog Relationships

The history of domestication of the dog has been reviewed in Chapter I. We must consider how changes in technology and social systems reflect the kind of dogs we see around us today. Very few breeds now serve the functions for which they were originally intended. A psychological analysis of man and his relationship with the dog has been reported (Hartley and Shames, 1959) in a study oriented toward the contemporary man-dog relationship in America. More than 40 per cent of families have a dog, larger dogs being popular in rural areas, and smaller dogs in cities. There are also regional variations; sled dogs in the north, foxhounds in Virginia, herding dogs on the plains, and coon hounds in rural areas. To study the preference for dogs in a particular group of society, a social ranking scale (social distance) was used to study the attitudes toward different ethnic groups. For each of twenty-two breeds of dogs, the respondents (a group of students) were asked to indicate how "close" they would allow them. The index of popularity was not the same as the American Kennel Club ranking, indicating subgroup studies can give widely differing results from the National data. Low correlations were found between liking a certain breed and actual familiarity with it.

In the social group sampled, relative familiarity with the different breeds of dogs tended to be similar among the respondents. Patterns of breed preference were similar, though not as much as the degree of familiarity. There was only a slight tendencey for familiarity to be associated with preference. A pictorial test was then employed. Cards on which pictures of the following breeds were depicted were given to the subjects: airedale, Chihuahua, Afghanhound, English bulldog, Pekingese, boxer, cairn terrier and standard poodle. The respondents were asked to indicate how they would feel about having one of these as a pet, a five-point gradient of attractiveness being used. Resultant coefficients confirmed the findings from the social distance scale in that a generalized nature of attitudes toward dogs exists. Some respondents gave different results, however, indicating that sometimes he may seem to like dogs, and sometimes to dislike them. An owner may on the whole like his dog, but at times dislikes him. In the pictorial group of dogs, there were four dogs that might appeal to masculinity and four that might appeal to femininity. As the social group consisted of fifty-eight men and fifty-four women, some sex differences might have been found, but this was not the case. No significant differences between sexes were found, except in two breeds; males preferred Boxers and females prefered Pekingese.

In general there is agreement that dogs perform useful functions and satisfy human needs either directly or symbolically, according to Bossard (1944), Burke (1903) and Lehman (1928).

These psychological reports stress that dogs serve their owners as a means of expressing their own aggressiveness, to provide the owners with something to dominate, or perhaps serve

124 CANINE BEHAVIOR

to these changes. Consequently, the function of the domesticated dog has changed during the development of human society, and such changes are in many instances reflected in the overt behavior of this animal. Heiman (1956) has discussed man-dog relationships from the psycho-analytical viewpoint. He describes a case where a female patient used her dog to express fantasies having reference to herself and to immediate relatives, to her desire to have a child, and to displaced desires. Displacement, identification and projection on to the dog of instinctual cravings occurred, so that the dog served as an important factor in the maintenance of psychological equilibrium. The dog is a better subject than a child for maintaining the patient's emotional equilibrium and displacing sado-masochistic conflict. The choice of a pet may be for the expression of conflict, to replace a lost object or libido, or be of phallic significance or is associated with fetishism, phobia, sexual perversion or totemism. Heiman notes a preponderance of female cases, probably due to the similarity between man-dog and mother-child relationships. The animal may represent a member of the family to a child, who may displace its frustrations of one of the family toward the pet. Identification with an animal in the adult may be a compromise effected with more regression than occurs with zoophobia; in zoophobia the animal serves as a barrier against incest, so that the patient may avoid incestuous and aggressive wishes and may find substitutive expression for them in the animal. Heiman concludes that the dog, as an individual totem (or talisman against death, i.e., protective), represents an important aid in sublimating innocuous forces incompatible with the civilized state of man. He observes that the dog is a better object for the patient's attentions than a child, for the child may be seriously influenced in such a psychopathic relationship. It would be interesting to investigate the behavior of the pet that is participant in such a relationship for behavioral adaptation and abnormality, as a result of an atypical psychosocial relationship with the owner, and with humans in general (Siegel, 1962; Speck, 1964).

Levinson (1962, 1963) has stated that pets can be useful in treating disturbed children or families. Some pets are better than others for helping children with their varying problems. Large animals are preferred by children having trouble getting along with people. Small animals are preferred by those with internal problems. Cats are the choice of children who are withdrawn. The temperament of a breed of dog should be carefully considered when choosing an animal for a pet. It is generally well recognized that pets are good for normal children, and they are being used in therapy for socially insecure or maladjusted children, with excellent results.

References

Bossard, J. H. S.: The mental hygiene of owning a dog. *Mental Hygiene, 28*:408-413, 1944.

Bowlby, J. L.: Critical phases in the development of social responses in man and other animals. Prospects in Psychiatric Research, *Proceedings First Conference of the Mental Health Research Fund,* J. M. Tanner, ed., Oxford, Blackwell Scientific Pub. Ltd., 1953.

Burke, W. F.: Children's thoughts, reactions and feelings toward pet dogs. *J. Genet. Psychol., 10*:489-511, 1903.

Hartley, E. L. and Shames, C.: Man and dog, a psychological analysis. *Gaines Vet. Symposium.,* Gaines, New York, 1959.

Heiman, M.: The relationship between man and dog. *Psychoanal. Quart., 25*:568-585, 1956.

Krushinskii, L. V.: *Animal Behavior.* New York, Consultant Bureau, 1962.

Lehman, H. C.: Child's attitude toward the dog versus the cat. *J. Genet. Psychol., 35*:67-72, 1928.

Levinson, B. M.: Pets help disturbed children. *Science News Letter, 84*:167, 1963.

Levinson, B. M.: The dog as a co-therapist. *Ment. Hyg., 40*:59-65, 1962.

Liddell, H. W.: *Experimental Neuroses in Animals and Man.* Springfield, Thomas, 1956.

Merrill, G. G.: Breaking the killing habit in dogs by inhibiting the conditioned reflex. *J. Amer. Vet. M. A., 107*:69-70, 1945.

Pettit, C.: Personal communication, Canine Defense League Training Centre, England, 1962.

Pfaffenberger, C. J.: Training Your Spaniel. New York, Putnam, 1947.

Pfaffenberger, C. F. and Scott, J. P.: The relationship between delayed socialization and trainability in guide dogs. *J. Genet. Psychol., 95*:145-155, 1959.

Scott, J. P.: Animal sexuality. In *The Encyclopedia of Sexual Behavior,* A. Ellis and A. Abarbanel, eds., New York, Hawtorn, 1961.

Scott, J. P.: The process of primary socialization in canine and human infants. *Monogr. Soc. Res. Child Development, 85*:28:1, 1963.

Siegel, A.: Researching the severely withdrawn through pet therapy. *Am. J. Psychiat., 118*:1045-6, 1962.

Speck, R. V.: Mental health problems involving the family, the pet, and the veterinarian. *J. Amer. Vet. M. A., 145*:2:150-154, 1964.

Chapter 9

CLASSIFICATION AND INTERPRETATION OF ABNORMAL ADULT BEHAVIOR PATTERNS

WHEN INTERPRETING abnormal behavior of the dog, several factors should be considered before a diagnosis may be made. These several factors, namely genetic constitution, early experience during the critical period of socialization and behavioral adaptation to the immediate environment, interact and their total effect is expressed in the overt behavior of the animal. The social relationship of the dog with the owner, whether it be hierarchically subordinate and overprotected or dominant and overprotective is also contributory.

Hebb's criteria may be applied to the dog as it is to man, where specific signs are characteristics of a true behavioral breakdown (see chapter 6).

To briefly consider these criteria, abnormal behavior is frequently seen in organic disease and, depending on the signs, several conditions should be considered: neoplasia of the CNS, for example, and cranial trauma, viral and toxic encephalopathies, idiopathic epilepsy, labyrinthinitis, hypocalcemia, hypoglycemia and adrenal insufficiency. Behavior in such cases is symptomatic and may be adaptive to the situation. For example, a lame dog will limp, a uremic dog will vomit, a dog with chronic pancreatitis will eat compulsively, although hysterical lameness, psychogenic vomiting and compulsive eating have been recorded in the dog as behavioral abnormalities where no pathologic lesions could be found. Differential diagnosis of organic disease from a non-organic behavioral disorder should therefore be undertaken with great care. It is possible that an animal with anxiety (by definition anxiety is a conditioned fear reaction, and even minor stimuli may cause its increase) as a result of emotional stress may revert to behavior (reversed fixation) previously associated with disease or trauma. Such cases have been seen in hysterical lameness and may be a care-seeking response to evoke sympathy from the owner. Strong rooting behavior present normally only in the neoate dog has been seen in fearful and timid adult dogs seeking the attention of the owner. What is to be diagnosed as abnormal behavior should be typically maladaptive to the situation and theretically fulfill Hebb's criteria. Few dogs develop such abnormal behavior patterns, but frequently due to repetitive stimulation, lack of escape and therefore lack of adaptation, the abnormality persists as a chronic deviation from the normal behavioral baseline.

It may be difficult to decide what prime factor triggered the onset of behavioral change and it may be that several interacting factors are involved. Genetic, social and early experiential trauma have been enumerated in previous chapters. Any sudden alteration in the social environment may also cause behavioral changes which are maladaptive; adaptation may later occur either spontaneously or when the environment reverts to the original state. Anorexia nervosa, extreme aggression and fear biting have been attributed to sudden environmental changes occuring in the home, i.e., visitors, human or animal, cause a sudden change in the social order within the closed community of the household.

To summarize these factors, we may say that the adult dog, having behavior patterns already moulded by genetic and early socio-environmental influences may have abnormal adult behavior patterns due to inheritance or psychological trauma during early postnatal development. Conversely we may have an animal that has typical adult behavior patterns but as a result of a sudden environmental change normal behavioral adaptation does not ocur and maladaptive behavior results. Sudden changes include acute psychological trauma which may persist as a conditioned emotional reaction (anxiety). Fixation follows, or displacement activity to an earlier behavior pattern. This behavior may be an attempt by the animal to adapt to the situation. Normally the animal would modify its behavior until an appropriate activity gives adaptation to the situation. Fixation (stereotyped response to a specific stimulus or accumulation of stimuli) may then occur which is adaptive to the situation, but if there is wide deviation from the normal original behavioral baseline, the behavior is maladaptive. Compulsive eating for example is adaptive behavior and may serve as an anxiety relief mechanism, but is abnormal behavior as such an activity deviates widely from the normal.

In Chapter 3 the normal behavior patterns have been described and spontaneous abnormalities of these basic patterns, where such deviations constitute abnormal behavior, have been discussed in Chapter 7.

In summary, the following list of adult behavior patterns is presented, and it will be noted that abnormalities and undesirable activities may arise in most categories which may be suppressed by early training but are harder to control at a later age. (Fox, 1963). Examples of these are given.

Aggressive (Agonistic) Behavior. Abnormal aggression occurs in displacement behavior where a human or animal is attacked by the domesticated dog who under normal circumstances would not show aggression. Such behavior may be an anxiety relief activity (fear biting) or be a display of social dominance.

Sexual. Deviations occur when the dog is in a closed social community and is more or less "imprinted" with the human in the domestic environment. Too early socialization with man and restricted socialization with dogs may cause this. Sexual behavior (submissive urination and clasping objects having the odour of the owner, or protecting the owner and home from strangers by aggression and territorial defensive behavior) may be directed towards the human as a true displacement activity as a result of inadequate socialization with its own species at an early age. Frigidity and inability to breed with other dogs is a common occurance in such cases.

Et-epimeletic (Care Seeking) Behavior. After weaning, the dog is normally independent, but too early socialization with man and overprotection (which acts as hierarchical dominance) by the owner may maintain the dog as a "juvenile." Reward, especially constant petting and hand feeding, reinforces care seeking behavior and many adult pets are maintained as permanent puppies. Such animals also develop abnormal agonistic and sexual activities.

Eliminative, Excretory and Ingestive (Oral) Behavior involves both the autonomic system and the emotionality of the animal. As the autonomic system is involved, true psychosomatic disorders may occur after appropriate repetitive stimulation followed by maladaptive behavior (see Chapter 7). Submissive urination, elimination during fear or conditioned anxiety, compulsive eating, anorexia nervosa and vomiting have been attributed to psychomatic derailment of the normal behavioral baseline (Chertok and Fontaine, 1963).

In conclusion, we have discussed how environmental stimuli modifying early experience and the genetic constitution of the animal may cause changes in behavior at the emotional and autonomic (internal environment) levels. The expression of the behavior trait may be one of attempted adaptation of the organism to the environmental change. By considering the several contributory factors involved and specific criteria of normality, we may be able to recognize and remedy the behavioral change if it be maladaptive and detrimental to the well being of the animal.

References

Chertok L., and Fontaine, M.: Psychosomatics in Veterinary Medicine. *J. Psychosom. Res.*, 7:229-235, 1963.

Fox, M. W.: Canine Behavior, Part II. Experimental and Clinical Abnormalities. *Mod. Vet. Prac.*, Sept. 41-47, 1963.

INDEX

131

OE